D0615379

GRAPHICAL SOLUTIONS

BY

CHARLES O. MACKEY, M.E.

Professor of Heat Power Engineering,
Cornell University

SECOND EDITION

NEW YORK

JOHN WILEY & SONS, Inc.

London: CHAPMAN & HALL, Limited

PRINTED IN THE UNITED STATES OF AMERICA

PREFACE TO SECOND EDITION

In this edition the discussion of the construction of alignment charts has been expanded. A complete explanation is given of the use of determinants in the graphical representation of equations of special form that contain as many as six variables. Projective transformation is discussed; this method may be used to construct alignment charts of convenient sizes and desirable proportions. In this expanded treatment, there are new illustrative examples and new exercises.

In response to an expressed need, a new chapter has been added which explains the fitting of empirical equations to periodic curves — curves which are composed of the repetition of values of one variable at regular, repeated intervals of a second variable. This new chapter, like all the chapters in the first edition, contains illustrative examples and exercises for solution by the student.

C. Osborn Mackey.

Ithaca, New York
January 3, 1944

PREFACE TO FIRST EDITION

Every engineer should receive some training in graphical and mechanical solutions. A graphical or mechanical representation of an equation which must be solved many times may be justified because the chances for error in solving the equation are minimized and speed and ease of solution are contributed. Chapters I through IV cover stationary adjacent scales, sliding scales, network charts, alignment charts, and combinations of these solutions.

The fitting of equations to experimental data is another important task that frequently confronts the engineer, and methods of determining the values of the constants in non-periodic equations are discussed in Chapter V.

This book is the outgrowth of a course offered for many years in the School of Mechanical Engineering at Cornell University, and I am greatly indebted to Mr. Frederic C. Evans and Professor Karl D. Wood, former teachers of this course, for instruction in the subject and for some of the material appearing in the text. As given at the present time, the course is elective to juniors and seniors and consists of two recitations per week for fifteen weeks. Enough material is furnished in the text for a longer course, however.

The book is not a *treatise* on graphical computations. I have made no attempt to read and abstract everything that has been written on this subject. Instead, the text contains the material believed to be sufficient for a well-rounded course. The treatment is elementary, and the mathematics simple. Most of the examples can be handled with a working knowledge of logarithms, algebra, and a few principles of plane geometry. By omitting those few problems in which the calculus is used, the course might very properly be offered to freshmen.

With the exception of the discussion of special-purpose slide rules, much of the material given in the text has been covered, in part, in the works of d'Ocagne, Lipka, Hewes and Seward, Peddle, and others. I believe that the space allotted to each subject is nearly in proportion to its importance to engineering students and engineers. The text contains material, in particular, that has been found by experience to be teachable.

I am indebted to Mrs. Lipka for permission to reproduce the logarithmic scales, furnished with this book, from the chart prepared by the late Professor Joseph Lipka, which originally appeared in his book " Graphical and Mechanical Computation."

C. OSBORN MACKEY.

Ithaca, New York.

CONTENTS

All illustrations are shown to a scale that is one-half of that used in preparing the original drawings, and the dimensions mentioned in the description of each figure are those of the original drawing or twice those of the actual reproduction.

GRAPHICAL SOLUTIONS

CHAPTER I

STATIONARY ADJACENT SCALES

1. (*a*) Before any graphical methods of solution are explained, many terms that will occur frequently must be defined.

A *graphical scale* is a line, curved or straight, upon which are marked strokes to correspond to a set of numbers arranged in order of magnitude. If each value of a variable, u, determines a single value of some function of the variable, $f(u)$, the function may be represented by a graphical scale. If the distances between successive strokes representing equal increments in the variable are equal, the scale is uniform; if these distances are unequal, the scale is nonuniform.

(*b*) The *scale modulus*,[1] m, is the ratio of the linear length of a segment of the scale to the range of the function of the variable represented in that distance.

A uniform scale, then, represents the function, $f(u) = u$. The L scale on the engineer's slide rule that shows a range of L from 0 to 10 in a distance of 25 cm. represents $f(L) = \dfrac{L}{10}$ with a scale modulus of 25 cm. The most common nonuniform scales are the power scales representing $f(u) = u^n$, with n other than unity, and the logarithmic scales representing $f(u) = \log u$. The C and D scales on the slide rule are logarithmic scales with a scale modulus of 25 cm. $\left(m = \dfrac{25 \text{ cm.}}{\log 10 - \log 1} \right)$. Note carefully, at this point, that although a graphical scale is marked with progressive values

---

[1] Some may prefer to call this the *functional modulus*.

1

of the variable, u, the scale modulus is the ratio of the length of the scale to the range of the *function* of the variable, $f(u)$, represented, and not the ratio of the length of the scale to the range of the *variable*, u, represented.

(c) If x represents any linear distance along a graphical scale measured from a reference point, or origin, then, by definition of the scale modulus, $x = mf(u)$, and this equation is called the equation of the scale. Note that, at the origin of the scale, $x = 0$, and $f(u) = 0$, but u need not be zero at this point; for example, if the equation of the scale is $x = m \log u$, the value of u represented at the origin of the scale is $u = 1.0$.

2. (a) A relation between two variables, u and v, of the form $f_1(u) = f_2(v)$ may be represented graphically on stationary adjacent scales, i.e., scales constructed on opposite sides of the same axis from the same origin with the same scale modulus.

In Fig. 1, $x = m_1 f_1(u)$ and $y = m_2 f_2(v)$, and if $m_1 = m_2$ then $f_1(u) = f_2(v)$.

FIG. 1.   Stationary adjacent scales.

(b) One principal use of stationary adjacent scales is in the conversion of units from one system to another, and many such scales will be found in engineering textbooks. Several examples will now be given to illustrate the construction and use of parallel adjacent scales:

(1) The following empirical equation gives the heat content of either saturated or superheated steam at pressures under 5 lb. per sq. in. abs. for temperatures up to 500 F. with an error of less than $\frac{1}{4}$ of 1 per cent when compared with the "Steam Tables" of J. H. Keenan:

$$h = 1059.2 + 0.45t$$

where h = the heat content, in B.t.u. per pound,

t = the temperature, in degrees Fahrenheit.

If temperatures from -20 F. to 100 F. are to be shown on the chart, the range of $f(t)$ or h is (1104.2 $-$ 1050.2), or 54. Using a scale modulus, m, of 0.1 in., this range would be shown in a scale length of 5.4 in. The equation of the upper scale is $x = 0.1h$, and the equation of the lower scale is $y = 105.92 + 0.045t$. Each of these scales is a uniform scale, and an increment in h of 1 B.t.u. per lb. is represented by a distance of 0.1 in., while an increment in t of 1 deg. F. is represented by a distance of 0.045 in. The scale for h starts with a value of h of 1050 and a corresponding value of $x = 105$ in.; locating one value on the t scale fixes the rest of that scale, so if $t = 0$, $y = 105.92$ in., and this value of t is 0.92 in. to the right of the point representing $h = 1050$. The finished chart is shown in Fig. 2.

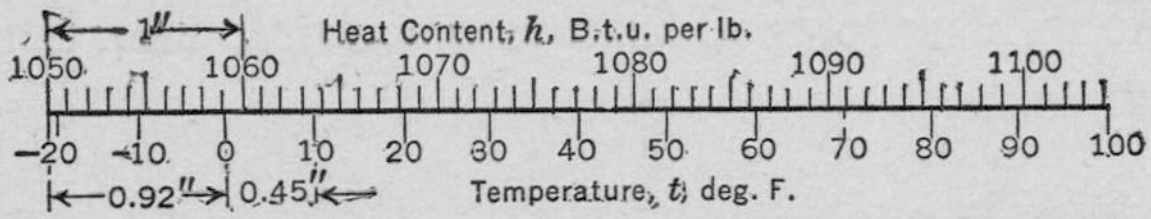

FIG. 2. The heat content of steam at low pressures.
$(h = 1059.2 + 0.45t)$

(2) The equation for velocity head in terms of velocity is

$$H = \frac{v^2}{2g} = \frac{v^2}{64.4}$$

where H = velocity head, in feet of fluid,

v = velocity, in feet per second.

If velocities from 0 to 12 are to be shown on the chart, the range of $f(v)$ and H is from 0 to 2.236; using a scale modulus, m, of 2 in., this range will be represented by a scale 4.47 in. long. The equation of the upper scale is $x = 2H$, and the equation of the lower scale is $y = \frac{2v^2}{64.4} = \frac{v^2}{32.2}$. The upper scale is a uniform scale with an increment in H of 1 ft.

represented in a distance of 2 in.; the lower scale is non-uniform, and the position of different values of v in this scale may be calculated from the equation of the scale as in the accompanying table. The finished chart is shown in

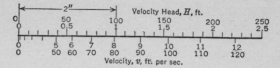

FIG. 3. The conversion of velocity into velocity head:

$$\left(H = \frac{v^2}{64.4} \right)$$

Fig. 3; an auxiliary scale has been added for greater values of v. Note that if v is multiplied by 10, H is multiplied by 100.

v	0	1	2	3	4	5	6	7	8	9	10	11	12
$y = \dfrac{v^2}{32.2}$	0	0.03	0.12	0.28	0.50	0.78	1.12	1.52	1.99	2.52	3.11	3.76	4.47

(c) The two preceding charts might have been drawn with logarithmic scales, after modifying the equations by taking logarithms of both sides, e.g., $\log h = \log (1059.2 + 0.45t)$. The uniform scale gives uniform accuracy in reading figures following the decimal point; i.e., 1.41 may be read on a uniform scale with the same accuracy as 10.41 or 10,000.41. The logarithmic scale, however, gives uniform accuracy in reading significant figures; i.e., 1.41 may be read with the same accuracy as 14.1 or 14,100. Since uniform accuracy in reading significant figures is usually desired in engineering problems, the logarithmic scale is usually preferred. On the other hand, the disadvantages of using logarithmic scales are that the zero value of the variable never appears on the scale and accurate interpolation is more difficult than on a uniform scale.

As an illustration of the use of logarithmic scales, the following empirical equation for the film coefficient of heat transfer on the water side of condenser tubes is charted:

$$h = 240 \left(\frac{v}{\mu}\right)^{0.8}$$

where h = the film coefficient of heat transfer, in B.t.u. per hour per degree Fahrenheit per square foot,

v = the velocity of the water, in feet per second,

μ = the absolute viscosity of the water at the film temperature, in centipoises.

The same equation, written in logarithmic form, follows:

$$\log h = \log 240 + 0.8 \log \left(\frac{v}{\mu}\right)$$

If a range of h from 100 to 1000 is to be shown, the range of $f(h)$ is $(3 - 2)$ or 1; using a scale modulus of 5 in., the length of the scale representing this range will be 5 in. The equation of the upper scale is $x = 5 \log h$, and in making the chart, a logarithmic scale with a scale base of 5 in. would be used. The equation of the lower scale is $y = 5 \log 240 + 4 \log \frac{v}{\mu}$; on this scale one complete cycle of logarithms $\bigg($as from $\frac{v}{\mu} = 0.5$ to $\frac{v}{\mu} = 5\bigg)$ is shown in a distance of 4 in., so a logarithmic scale on a scale base of 4 in. must be used for the $\frac{v}{\mu}$ scale. Locating one value of $\left(\frac{v}{\mu}\right)$ in the proper position relative to the h scale is necessary; with $\left(\frac{v}{\mu}\right) = 1.0$, $y = 11.90$ in., while the point representing $h = 100$ is 10 in. from the origin; therefore, the point representing a value of $\left(\frac{v}{\mu}\right) = 1$ must be located 1.90 in. to the right of the point representing $h = 100$. The finished chart is shown in Fig. 4. Note that although the modulus of the $\frac{v}{\mu}$ scale is 5 in., the distance in which one cycle of logarithms is shown, or the *scale base*, is 4 in.

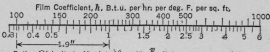

FIG. 4. The film coefficient of heat transfer on the water side of condenser tubes.

$$\left[h = 240\left(\frac{v}{\mu}\right)^{0.8} \right]$$

3. A few suggestions concerning the construction of any graphical scale may prove helpful to the beginner at this point. On scales constructed by hand, the distance between adjacent strokes should not be less than 0.05 in. nor more than about 0.4 in. The space between units should usually be divided into 5 or 10 intervals. The strokes should be narrow; the length of the short strokes should be about 0.1 in. and that of the longer strokes about 0.15 in. The distance between adjacent numbers marked on the scale should not be much less than 0.2 in. The decimal point should always be indicated. These suggestions or rules are highly arbitrary, and there are exceptions to most of them, but if they are followed approximately, the appearance and utility of any scales constructed may be improved.

4. *Exercises.* (The length of the scales in the charts of the exercises should not exceed 10 in.)

(1) Prepare a chart with adjacent uniform scales to solve the empirical equation for the latent heat of steam, $r = 1091.2 - 0.55t$. Show a range of t from -20 F. to 100 F.

(2) Prepare a chart with adjacent scales to solve the equation for compression ratio, $r = \dfrac{1 + c}{c}$. Show a range in clearance, c, from 0.065 to 0.11.

(3) Prepare a chart with adjacent logarithmic scales to convert pressure from the units of pounds per square inch to inches of mercury at 32 F. Show a range from 1 to 15 lb. per sq. in.

(4) Prepare a chart with adjacent uniform scales to convert temperature from degrees Fahrenheit into degrees Centigrade. Show a range from −20 F. to 100 F.

(5) Prepare a chart with adjacent logarithmic scales to solve the equation for the friction factor of smooth pipes, $f = \dfrac{0.049}{(Re)^{0.2}}$. Show a range of Reynolds' number, Re, from 5000 to 200,000.

(6) Prepare a chart with adjacent scales to give the logarithms to the base 10 of numbers from 1 to 10.

(7) Prepare a chart with adjacent scales to give the sines of angles from 1 to 90 deg.

(8) Prepare a chart with adjacent scales to give the tangents of angles from 6 to 45 deg.

(9) Prepare a chart with adjacent logarithmic scales to give the areas of circles with diameters from 1 to 10 in.

(10) Prepare a chart with adjacent scales to give the ideal velocity attained by a fluid expanding adiabatically in a nozzle; the velocity, in feet per second, $v = 223.7 \sqrt{\Delta h}$, where $\Delta h =$ the drop in heat content, in B.t.u. per pound (100 to 400).

CHAPTER II

SLIDING SCALES

5. (a) *Sliding scales* may be used to solve many equations of engineering importance. The engineer's slide rule is used for performing multiplication and division, for raising numbers to powers and extracting roots, and for finding logarithms and trigonometric functions. If one equation is to be solved many times, a special-purpose slide rule, or a slide rule that solves only this equation, may be desirable. In this text only slide rules with straight parallel scales will be considered, although circular, spiral, and cylindrical slide rules have been constructed.

(b) Before any specific slide rule is considered, the general form of the equation that may be solved using one stationary

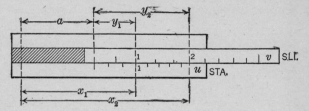

FIG. 5. Slide rule with one sliding scale and one stationary scale.

scale and one sliding scale will be developed. In the slide rule of Fig. 5, the stationary member carries a graphical scale for some function of the variable u, while the sliding member carries a graphical scale for some function of the variable v. For the setting represented in the sketch, the origins of these scales are displaced any distance, a inches. The equation of the stationary scale is $x = m_1 f_1(u)$, assuming the modulus of this scale to be m_1 inches; the equation of the sliding scale is similarly, $y = m_2 f_2(v)$. Any two reference sections on the scales, such as 1 and 2, may be chosen; the

8

values of u and v appearing at these sections are labelled with corresponding subscripts. Then,

$$x_1 - y_1 = x_2 - y_2 = a$$

But
$$x_1 = m_1 f_1(u_1)$$
$$x_2 = m_1 f_1(u_2)$$
$$y_1 = m_2 f_2(v_1)$$

and
$$y_2 = m_2 f_2(v_2)$$

Then, $m_1 f_1(u_1) - m_2 f_2(v_1) = m_1 f_1(u_2) - m_2 f_2(v_2)$

If the moduli of the two scales are equal, i.e., if $m_1 = m_2$,

$$f_1(u_1) - f_2(v_1) = f_1(u_2) - f_2(v_2) \quad \ldots \ldots (1)$$

The latter equation is the form of the relation between the variables u and v that may be solved with one stationary scale and one sliding scale.

(c) Many different types of graphical scales might be used on such a slide rule, but only a few important or interesting combinations are considered here.

If $f_1(u) = u$ and $f_2(v) = v$, both scales are *uniform*, and such a slide rule is shown in Fig. 6. If section 1 is taken at

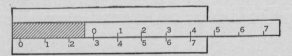

FIG. 6. Slide rule with two uniform scales.

the origin of the sliding scale with 2 representing any other section, then, from Eq. (1),

$$u_1 = u_2 - v_2 \ldots \ldots \ldots \ldots (2a)$$
or
$$u_2 = u_1 + v_2 \ldots \ldots \ldots \ldots (2b)$$

A slide rule with uniform scales could then be used for addition and subtraction, but any useful application is clearly limited by the failure to give satisfactory accuracy in a reasonable length.

(*d*) If $f_1(u) = \dfrac{1}{u}$ and $f_2(v) = \dfrac{1}{v}$, the slide rule carries reciprocal scales as shown in Fig. 7.   With section 1 taken at the

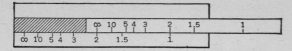

FIG. 7:   Slide rule with two reciprocal scales.

origin of the v scale ($v = \infty$) and 2 representing any other section, from Eq. (1),

$$\frac{1}{u_1} - \frac{1}{\infty} = \frac{1}{u_2} - \frac{1}{v_2} \quad \cdots \cdots \cdots \quad (3a)$$

or
$$\frac{1}{u_2} = \frac{1}{u_1} + \frac{1}{v_2}. \quad \cdots \cdots \cdots \cdots \quad (3b)$$

This slide rule might be used to find the sum of two resistances in parallel $\left(\dfrac{1}{R} = \dfrac{1}{R_1} + \dfrac{1}{R_2}\right)$ or to solve the common lens equation $\left(\dfrac{1}{f} = \dfrac{1}{p} + \dfrac{1}{q}\right)$.   By continued settings, a similar slide rule might also be used to find the overall coefficient of heat transfer in terms of the various film coefficients and thermal conductances,

$$\frac{1}{U} = \frac{1}{h_1} + \frac{L}{k} + \frac{1}{h_2}$$

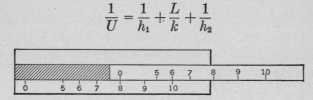

FIG. 8.   Slide rule with two squared scales:

(*e*) If $f_1(u) = u^2$ and $f_2(v) = v^2$, the slide rule carries squared scales as shown in Fig. 8.   With section 1 at the origin of the v scale and 2 any other section, from Eq. (1),

$$u_1{}^2 = u_2{}^2 - v_2{}^2 \quad \cdots \cdots \cdots \quad (4a)$$
or
$$u_2{}^2 = u_1{}^2 + v_2{}^2 \quad \cdots \cdots \cdots \quad (4b)$$

A slide rule with squared scales, then, solves the right triangle, and such scales appear on some of the log log rules.

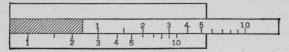

FIG. 9. Slide rule with two logarithmic scales.

(f) In Fig. 9 is shown a slide rule with logarithmic scales; here, $f_1(u) = \log u$ and $f_2(v) = \log v$. With section 1 at the origin of the v scale ($v = 1$) and 2 any other section,

$$\log u_1 - \log 1 = \log u_2 - \log v_2 \quad . \quad . \quad . \quad . \quad (5a)$$

or
$$u_1 = \frac{u_2}{v_2}. \quad . \quad . \quad . \quad . \quad . \quad . \quad . \quad (5b)$$

or
$$u_2 = u_1 v_2 \quad . \quad . \quad . \quad . \quad . \quad . \quad . \quad (5c)$$

A sliding log scale used in conjunction with a stationary log scale performs division and multiplication, and the combination is frequently used.

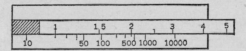

FIG. 10. Slide rule with stationary log log scale and sliding log scale.

(g) In Fig. 10, a slide rule with one log log scale and one log scale is shown; here, $f_1(u) = \log (\log u)$ and $f_2(v) = \log v$. With section 1 at the origin of the v scale ($v = 1$) and 2 representing any other section,

$$\log (\log u_1) - \log 1 = \log (\log u_2) - \log v_2 \quad . \quad . \quad (6a)$$

or
$$\log u_1^{v_2} = \log u_2 \quad . \quad . \quad . \quad . \quad . \quad . \quad . \quad (6b)$$

or
$$u_2 = (u_1)^{v_2} \quad . \quad . \quad . \quad . \quad . \quad . \quad . \quad (6c)$$

or
$$u_1 = (u_2)^{1/v_2} \quad . \quad . \quad . \quad . \quad . \quad . \quad . \quad (6d)$$

or
$$v_2 = \log_{u_1} u_2 \quad . \quad . \quad . \quad . \quad . \quad . \quad . \quad (6e)$$

As shown by the above equations, a slide rule with one log log and one log scale may be used to raise numbers to powers, extract roots, and find logarithms to any base. These are important uses of the engineer's log log slide rule.

6. *Exercises.*

(1) Lay out the two scales for a slide rule to solve the equation,

$$c = \sqrt{\frac{a}{b}}.$$

(2) Lay out the two scales for a slide rule to solve the equation, $b = a \cos c$.

(3) Lay out the two scales for a slide rule to solve the equation, $a = bc^{\frac{3}{2}}$.

7. The construction and use of a special-purpose slide rule as contrasted with the use of the engineer's log log rule to solve a given equation repeatedly may frequently be justified. In the first place, the decimal point may be shown directly on the special-purpose rule. Also one scale for a function of a variable will suffice on a special-purpose rule; for example if, the function of d, $\left(\dfrac{d + 3.6}{d^5}\right)$, appears in an equation, one scale labelled with values of d will represent this function on a special rule whereas a number of settings on the rule and addition external to the rule must be performed if the value of this function is to be found on the log log rule. Also the special slide rule may replace the use of the log log rule *and* tables or charts. For example, if d in the above function refers to the actual inside diameter of pipe, the scale on the special rule may be labelled with values of the nominal diameter, whereas a table of pipe sizes in addition to the log log rule would be necessary to give equivalent information; again if some property of a fluid, such as the latent heat of steam, depending upon some other observed property, such as temperature, enters an equation, the scale for latent heat on the special rule may be labelled with the values of temperature instead of latent heat, and reference to a steam table in the solution of the equation may be eliminated. Also, greater accuracy may be obtained on a special slide rule when the distance in which the range of a given variable is represented exceeds the distance representing the same range on the scale of the log log rule.

8. (*a*) The type of equation connecting *three* variables that may be solved using a special-purpose slide rule with two stationary scales, one sliding scale, and an arrow on the sliding scale will next be developed. In Fig. 11 the lower

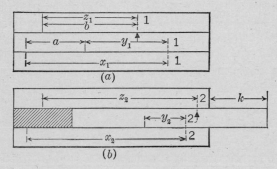

(a)

(b)

FIG. 11.   Slide rule with two stationary scales and one sliding scale
(three variables).

stationary segment carries a graphical scale for the variable *u* with an equation of the scale, $x = mf_1(u)$. The slide carries a graphical scale for the variable *v* with an equation, $y = mf_2(v)$. The upper stationary segment bears a graphical scale for the variable *w* with the equation, $z = mf_3(w)$. The same modulus is used on all three scales. In the position of the slide shown in Fig. 11a, the origin of the *v* scale is shown *a* inches to the right of the origin of the *u* scale, and, in the same position, the arrow on the sliding scale is *b* inches to the right of the origin of the *w* scale. For this position, taking any section, 1, as shown,

$$x_1 - y_1 = a$$

and
$$z_1 = b$$

or
$$mf_1(u_1) - mf_2(v_1) = a \quad \ldots \ldots \ldots \quad (7a)$$

and
$$mf_3(w_1) = b \quad \ldots \ldots \ldots \quad (7b)$$

After the slide is moved k inches to the right, as shown in Fig. 11b, with 2 representing some new section,

$$x_2 - y_2 = a + k$$

and
$$z_2 = b + k$$

or
$$mf_1(u_2) - mf_2(v_2) = a + k \quad \ldots \ldots \ldots \text{(8a)}$$

and
$$mf_3(w_2) = b + k \quad \ldots \ldots \ldots \text{(8b)}$$

In order that the same relation between u, v, and w is obtained for any setting of the sliding scale, k must be eliminated from Eqs. (8a) and (8b); by subtracting either (7b) from (7a), or (8b) from (8a), the following relation is obtained:

$$mf_1(u) - mf_2(v) - mf_3(w) = a - b$$

or
$$f_1(u) - f_2(v) - f_3(w) = \frac{a - b}{m} \quad \ldots \ldots \text{(9)}$$

In using the special slide rule to solve this equation, the value of v on the sliding scale is set over the value of u on the lower stationary scale, and the value of w is read above the arrow on the upper stationary scale.

Any equation involving three variables that can be written in the form of Eq. (9) may be solved on a special slide rule like that shown in Fig. 11. The steps to be followed in laying out the scales will be explained, in general, and also with a specific example.

First, calculate the ranges of the functions of the three variables; if the allowable or desirable length of the rule is known, this length and the greatest range will fix the common scale modulus, m.

Second, write the equations of the three scales.

Third, lay out the two stationary scales.

Fourth, lay out the sliding scale; note that the only consideration involved in locating this scale is that of keeping it on the paper, but once the scale is located, the distance between the origins of this scale and of the lower stationary scale is fixed, or a in Eq. (9) is fixed.

Fifth, solve Eq. (9) for b, and locate the arrow on the sliding scale.

Sixth, check the scale layout and the location of the arrow with several examples. Note that, if the arrow is placed on the sliding scale before the scales are mounted on the slide-rule blank, the upper and lower stationary scales must be in the same relative position when mounted as when drawn.

(b) As a specific example, consider the design of a special-purpose rule to solve the Unwin-Babcock formula for the flow of low-pressure steam in pipes: Assume a density of 0.04 lb. per cu. ft. for the low-pressure steam; then this formula becomes

$$p = 0.00145 w^2 \left(\frac{d + 3.6}{d^6} \right)$$

in which $p =$ the friction drop in pressure, in ounces per square inch per 100 ft. of pipe,

$w =$ the rate of steam flow, in pounds per hour,

$d =$ the actual inside diameter of the pipe, in inches.

Rewriting this equation in logarithmic form,

$$\log p = \log 0.00145 + \log w^2 + \log \left(\frac{d + 3.6}{d^6} \right)$$

By comparing this equation with Eq. (9), note that there is some choice in the location and equations of the three scales; e.g., $f_1(u)$ might be taken to correspond to $\log p$, $f_2(v)$ to $\log w^2$, $f_3(w)$ to $\log \frac{d + 3.6}{d^6}$; then $\frac{a - b}{m} = \log 0.00145$. If this selection were made, however, the scale for diameter would show increasing values of diameter from right to left. There will probably be a smaller chance for error in the use of the rule if all scales show increasing values of the variable from left to right; it will be better, then, to take

$$f_1(u) = \log w^2, f_2(v) = -\log\left(\frac{d + 3.6}{d^6}\right) = \log\left(\frac{d^6}{d + 3.6}\right),$$

$$f_3(w) = \log p, \quad \text{and} \quad \frac{a - b}{m} = -\log 0.00145 = 2.839$$

The accompanying table shows the calculation of the scale modulus and the equations of the three scales. The greatest range of the function of the variable, for the limits given, is 6.602; for a 10-in. rule, a scale modulus of 1.5 in. may then be used, since the length of the longest scale will be 9.90 in.

Variable	Limits of the variable	Function of the variable	Range of the function	Modulus	Equation of the scale
w	3 to 6000	$\log w^2$	7.556−0.954 =6.602	1.5	$3 \log w$
d	0.824 to 12.000	$\log\left(\frac{d^6}{d+3.6}\right)$	5.281−(−1.156) =6.337	1.5	$1.5 \log\left(\frac{d^6}{d+3.6}\right)$
p	0.01 to 10	$\log p$	1.00−(−2.00) =3.00	1.5	$1.5 \log p$

The lower stationary scale for w may next be laid out. This is a logarithmic scale on a 3-in. scale base. It is desirable to label the sliding scale for diameter with values of the nominal diameter instead of the actual inside diameter, and the calculation of the positions of the different nominal diameters in accordance with the equation of the scale is shown in tabular form for standard wrought-iron pipe.

The upper stationary scale for p is a logarithmic scale on a 1.5-in. scale base. In the design of the slide rule in Fig. 12, a nominal diameter of 1 in. ($d = 1.049$) is placed over a value of w of 10; referring to Fig. 11a, this location fixes the distance between the origin of the sliding scale and the origin of the lower stationary scale at a value of $a = 3 \log 10 -$ $1.5 \log\left(\frac{1.049^6}{1.049 + 3.6}\right) = 3.81$ in. But $(a - b)$ must equal

2.839m or 4.26 in.; therefore b = 3.81 − 4.26 = −0.45 in., or the direct reading arrow on the upper edge of the sliding

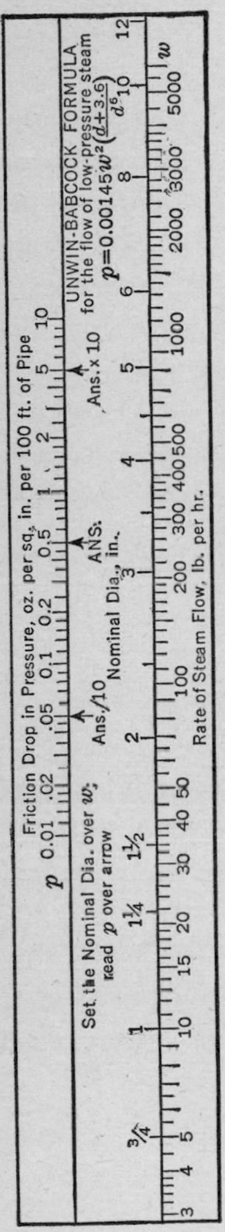

Nominal diameter d_n	Actual inside diameter d	$y = 1.5 \log \left(\dfrac{d^6}{d + 3.6} \right)$
$\frac{3}{4}$	0.824	−1.73
1	1.049	−0.81
$1\frac{1}{4}$	1.38	+0.21
$1\frac{1}{2}$	1.61	0.79
2	2.067	1.71
$2\frac{1}{2}$	2.469	2.35
3	3.068	3.15
$3\frac{1}{2}$	3.548	3.67
4	4.026	4.12
$4\frac{1}{2}$	4.506	4.51
5	5.047	4.92
6	6.065	5.57
8	8.071	6.56
10	10.192	7.36
12	12.000	7.92

FIG. 12. Slide rule solving the Unwin-Babcock formula.

scale must be placed 0.45 in. to the left of the origin of the upper stationary scale, i.e., 0.45 in. to the left of p = 1.

The direct reading arrow may run off the scale at times, so other arrows may be placed as shown in Fig. 12 to give the answer multiplied or divided by 10; in this case, these two arrows are placed 1.5 in. to the right and to the left, respectively, of the direct reading arrow. When these arrows are used, the length of the upper stationary scale on many slide rules may be decreased if desired.

In order to check the location of the direct reading arrow, substitute w = 10 and d = 1.049 in the equation for pressure drop and find p = 0.505. In mounting the scales on the slide-rule blank, the upper and lower stationary scales must be placed in the same relative position as that shown in Fig. 12.

9. The slide-rule blanks upon which the scales are mounted may be constructed of wood, or satisfactory blanks may be made by gluing together several layers of cardboard. By varying the widths of the strips, as shown in Fig. 13, the tongues and grooves may be formed. The scales may also be printed on opaque celluloid and, by rivetting transparent celluloid to the stationary scales, satisfactory rules may be cheaply constructed in large numbers.

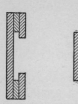

FIG. 13. Cross-section of a slide rule with one slide.

10. *Exercises.* (It is suggested that the scales be designed for a slide-rule blank about 10 in. long; limiting values of the variables are also given. However, the length of the rule and the limits of the variables may be changed if desirable.)

Design slide rules to solve the following formulas:

(1) $p = 0.000822 \dfrac{v^{1.77}}{d^{1.275}}$; friction drop in pressure in hot water

pipes, p, in inches per foot (0.005 to 1.5); velocity of water, v, in inches per second (4 to 100); actual inside diameter of pipe, d (show nominal diameters of standard wrought pipe from $\frac{1}{2}$ to 6 in.).

(2) B.H.P. $= \dfrac{2\pi NT}{33,000}$; brake horsepower, B.H.P. (10 to 400);

engine speed, N, in revolutions per minute (200 to 5000); torque, T, in pound-feet (15 to 500).

(3) $P = \dfrac{d^2 n}{2.5}$; S.A.E. horsepower, P (5 to 50); bore, d, in

inches (1 to 5); number of cylinders, n (1 to 16).

(4) $Q = 3.33b\,H^{\frac{3}{2}}$; rate of discharge from rectangular suppressed weir, Q, in cubic feet per second (1 to 50); width of weir crest, b, in feet (0.5 to 10); head, H, in feet (0.2 to 6).

(5) $p = \dfrac{Q^{1.86}}{5.7\,d^5}$; friction drop in pressure in round air ducts, p,

in inches of water per 100 ft. of duct (0.01 to 10); rate of flow, Q, in cubic feet per minute (50 to 300,000); diameter of duct, d, in inches (4 to 100).

(6) $\delta = \dfrac{p}{0.753\,(t + 460)}$; the density of dry air, δ, in pounds per cubic foot (0.06 to 0.09); the pressure of the dry air, p, in inches of mercury, absolute (25 to 35); the temperature of the air, t, in degrees Fahrenheit (0 to 140).

(7) $\dfrac{P}{A} = \dfrac{16{,}250}{1 + \dfrac{L^2}{11{,}000\,r^2}}$; the allowable load on steel columns per

unit area of cross-section, $\dfrac{P}{A}$, in pounds per square inch (7000 to 16,000); length of the column, L, in inches (12 to 600); least radius of gyration, r, in inches (0.5 to 5). Locate a secondary arrow on the rule to show when a value of $\dfrac{L}{r}$ of 120 is exceeded.

(8) $\dfrac{\mu}{\delta} = 0.00218t - \dfrac{1.979}{t}$; the absolute viscosity, μ, in poises (0.1 to 3); the density, δ, in grams per cubic centimeter (0.6 to 1.0); the time, t, in Saybolt seconds (50 to 1000).

(9) $\sqrt{H} = \dfrac{B}{3.33\,(A - 0.6\,\sqrt{A})}$; empirical equation for chimney height, H, in feet (50 to 200); boiler horsepower, B (50 to 400); inside area of cross-section, A, in square feet (5 to 18).

(10) $e = 1 - \left(\dfrac{1}{r}\right)^{\gamma-1}$; thermal efficiency of ideal Otto engine, e (0.24 to 0.60); compression ratio, r (4 to 8); ratio of specific heats, γ (1.2 to 1.4).

11. (*a*) An equation containing *four* variables may be solved on a slide rule having two stationary scales and one sliding scale by replacing the arrow, shown in Fig. 11, by a graphical scale. In using such a rule, the value of one variable, shown along the lower edge of the sliding scale, is placed above the value of a second variable, shown on the lower stationary scale; then, immediately above the value of a third variable, shown along the upper edge of the sliding scale, read the value of the fourth variable to satisfy the equation.

In Fig. 14, the lower stationary segment carries a graphical scale for the variable u with an equation of the scale

$x = mf_1(u)$. There are two scales on the slide; the equation of the lower scale is $y = mf_2(v)$, and the equation of the scale along the upper edge of the slide is $r = mf_4(n)$. The equation of the upper stationary scale is $z = mf_3(w)$. The same modulus, m, is used on all four scales.

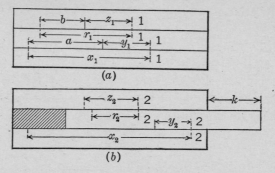

(a)

(b)

Fig. 14.   Slide rule with two stationary scales and two scales on the slide (four variables).

With the slide in the position shown in Fig. 14a, the origin of the v scale is a inches to the right of the origin of the u scale, and, the origin of the w scale is b inches to the right of the origin of the n scale.   For this position, take any setting such as 1; then

$$x_1 - y_1 = a$$
and
$$r_1 - z_1 = b$$
or
$$mf_1(u_1) - mf_2(v_1) = a \quad \ldots \ldots \quad (10a)$$
and
$$mf_4(n_1) - mf_3(w_1) = b \quad \ldots \ldots \quad (10b)$$

After the slide is moved k inches to the right, as shown in Fig. 14b, with 2 representing some new setting,

$$x_2 - y_2 = a + k$$
and
$$r_2 - z_2 = b - k$$
or
$$mf_1(u_2) - mf_2(v_2) = a + k \quad \ldots \ldots \quad (11a)$$
and
$$mf_4(n_2) - mf_3(w_2) = b - k \quad \ldots \ldots \quad (11b)$$

Eliminating k by adding (11b) and (11a),

$$mf_1(u) - mf_2(v) + mf_4(n) - mf_3(w) = a + b$$

or $$f_1(u) - f_2(v) + f_4(n) - f_3(w) = \frac{a+b}{m} \quad . \quad . \quad . \quad (12)$$

Any equation involving four variables that can be written in the form of Eq. (12) may be solved on a special slide rule designed like the one shown in Fig. 14.

(b) As an illustration, consider the design of a special slide rule to solve the Lewis formula for the strength of spur gears. Assuming that the width of the face of the gear is three times the circular pitch and that the teeth are 14½-deg. or 15-deg. involutes, this formula becomes

$$S = \frac{2Tp_d{}^3}{3\pi^2(0.124N - 0.684)}$$

in which S = the stress in pounds per square inch,

T = the torque, in pound-inches,

p_d = the diametral pitch, or the ratio of the number of teeth to the diameter of the pitch circle,

N = the number of teeth.

The same equation in logarithmic form is

$$\log(0.124N - 0.684) - \log T + \log S - 3\log p_d = \log\frac{2}{3\pi^2}$$

Compare this equation with Eq. (12), and note that $f_1(u)$ corresponds to $\log(0.124N - 0.684)$, $f_2(v)$ to $\log T$, $f_4(n)$ to $\log S$, $f_3(w)$ to $3\log p_d$, and $\frac{a+b}{m} = \log\frac{2}{3\pi^2} = -1.17$. The accompanying table shows the calculation of the common scale modulus and the equations of the four scales.

For the given limits of the variables, the greatest range of any function is 2.535; a scale modulus of 4 in. is chosen, and the length of the longest scale is 10.14 in. The lower stationary scale may be prepared from the accompanying

Variable	Limits of the variable	Function of the variable	Range of the function	Modulus	Equation of the scale
N	12 to 200	log (0.124N − 0.684)	$\log\dfrac{24.116}{0.804} =$ 1.477	4	4 log (0.124N − 0.684)
T	200 to 50,000	log T	$\log\dfrac{50,000}{200} =$ 2.398	4	4 log T
S	1000 to 100,000	log S	$\log\dfrac{100,000}{1000} =$ 2.000	4	4 log S
p_d	2 to 14	3 log p_d	$3\log\dfrac{14}{2} =$ 2.535	4	12 log p_d

N	$x = 4\log$ (0.124N − 0.684)	N	$x = 4\log$ (0.124N − 0.684)
12	−0.38 in.	60	3.32
13	−0.13	70	3.61
14	+0.09	80	3.86
15	0.28	90	4.08
20	1.02	100	4.27
25	1.53	110	4.45
30	1.93	120	4.61
35	2.25	130	4.75
40	2.52	140	4.89
45	2.76	150	5.02
50	2.97	200	5.53

table. The scales along both the lower and upper edges of the slide are logarithmic with a scale base of 4 in. If a value

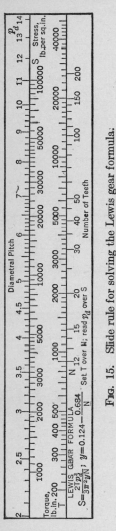

Fig. 15. Slide rule for solving the Lewis gear formula.

of T of 2000 is placed over a value of N of 20 as shown in Fig. 15, the distance between the origins of these scales, a, is equal to 4 log (0.124 × 20 − 0.684) − 4 log 2000 or −12.18 in.; therefore, $(-12.18 + b)$ must equal $4(-1.17)$ or −4.68. The distance between the origins of the two top scales must be $b = 7.50$ in. The scale for p_d is logarithmic with a scale base of 12 in. In order to locate the proper position of this scale, note that $S = 1000$ is 4 log 1000 or 12.00 in. from the origin of the S scale; a value of $p_d = 2$ is 12 log 2 = 3.61 in. from the origin of the p_d scale; therefore, if the point representing $p_d = 2$ is placed 0.89 in. to the left of the point representing $S = 1000$, the value of b will be 7.50 in. With this point located the rest of the scale may be laid out. The finished design is shown in Fig. 15. The location of the scales should be checked with an example; if $N = 20$, $T = 2000$, and $S = 10,000$, a solution of the formula gives $p_d = 5.1$, and the slide rule gives the same result.

12. Exercises. Design slide rules to solve the following formulas:

(1) $p = \dfrac{0.000058}{\delta} w^2 \left(\dfrac{d + 3.6}{d^6}\right)$; the friction drop in pressure in steam pipes, p, in ounces per square inch per 100 ft. (0.01 to 10); the density of the steam, δ, in pounds per cubic foot (0.03 to 0.5); the rate of flow, w, in pounds per hour (3 to 6000); the actual

28/00

inside diameter of the pipe, d, in inches (show nominal diameters of standard wrought pipe from $\frac{3}{4}$ to 12 in.).

(2) $v = \dfrac{dN}{336R}$; the speed of an automobile, v, in miles per hour (5 to 100); diameter of the tires, d, in inches (20 to 40); engine speed, N, in r.p.m. (200 to 5000); overall gear ratio, R (2 to 12).

(3) $D = \dfrac{\pi d^2 nl}{4}$; the piston displacement, D, in cubic inches (30 to 400); the bore, d, in inches (2 to $4\frac{1}{8}$ by steps of $\frac{1}{8}$ in.); the number of cylinders, n (4 to 8); the length of stroke, l, in inches ($2\frac{1}{2}$ to 5 by steps of $\frac{1}{8}$ in.).

(4) $p_m = \dfrac{792{,}000 \ (\text{H.P.})}{DN}$; the mean effective pressure of four-cycle engines, p_m, in pounds per square inch (10 to 200); the horsepower, H.P. (10 to 300); the piston displacement, D, in cubic inches (30 to 400); the engine speed, N, in r.p.m. (200 to 5000).

(5) $L = 0.00119 C_L S V^2$; the lifting force, L, in pounds (400 to 80,000); the lift coefficient, C_L (0.1 to 4); the wing area, S, in square feet (40 to 8000); the air speed, V, in miles per hour (30 to 400).

(6) B.H.P. $= \dfrac{2\pi P r N}{396{,}000}$; the brake horsepower, B.H.P. (10 to 400); the net load on a dynamometer, P, in pounds (5 to 500); the dynamometer arm, r, in inches (10 to 50); the engine speed, N, in r.p.m. (100 to 5000).

(7) $N_S = \dfrac{N P^{\frac{1}{2}}}{H^{\frac{5}{4}}}$; the characteristic speed of water turbines, N_S, in r.p.m. (3 to 200); the rotative speed, N, in r.p.m. (50 to 1000); the brake horsepower, P (20 to 2000); the effective head, H, in feet (5 to 1500).

(8) $w = \dfrac{0.622 \,(\text{R.H.})\, p}{p_b - (\text{R.H.})\, p}$; the specific humidity, or the weight of water vapor mixed with each pound of dry air, w, in pounds (0.001 to 0.1); the relative humidity, R.H., as a decimal (0.1 to 1.0); the barometric or total pressure, p_b, in inches of mercury, absolute (25 to 32); the pressure of saturated water vapor at the dry-bulb temperature, p, in inches of mercury, absolute (instead of a scale for p, show on the rule a scale for dry-bulb temperature, which determines p, from 32 F. to 120 F.).

13. (*a*) Equations containing *five* or *six* variables may be solved on special slide rules having two stationary scales and two sliding scales. In Fig. 16, a slide rule solving an equation of *five* variables is shown. The top and bottom

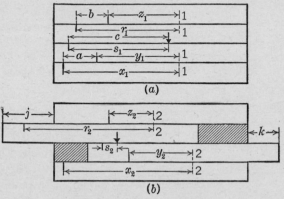

Fig. 16. Slide rule with two stationary scales and two slides (five variables).

scales are stationary, and the two adjacent middle scales slide. The bottom stationary segment carries a graphical scale for u, the equation of which is $x = mf_1(u)$. Along the bottom edge of the lower slide there is a scale for v, with the equation $y = mf_2(v)$. Along the top edge of this lower slide there is a scale for p such that $s = mf_5(p)$. The arrow is placed along the lower edge of the upper slide; along the top edge of this slide there is a scale for n, with the equation $r = mf_4(n)$. The top stationary scale is for w with the equation $z = mf_3(w)$. A common modulus is used on all five scales.

Using such a rule, the lower slide is adjusted until the given value of v is immediately above the given value of u; the upper slide is set so that n is under w, then the value of p satisfying the equation is found under the arrow.

With the slides in the position shown in Fig. 16*a*, the origin of the v scale is a inches to the right of the origin of the u scale, the origin of the w scale is b inches to the right of the origin of the n scale, and the arrow is c inches to the right of the origin of the p scale. For this position, take any setting such as 1; then

$$x_1 - y_1 = a$$
$$s_1 = c$$

and $$r_1 - z_1 = b$$

or $$mf_1(u_1) - mf_2(v_1) = a \quad \cdots \cdots \quad (13a)$$
$$mf_5(p_1) = c \quad \cdots \cdots \cdots \quad (13b)$$

and $$mf_4(n_1) - mf_3(w_1) = b \quad \cdots \cdots \quad (13c)$$

After the lower slide is moved k inches to the right, and the upper slide j inches to the left, as shown in Fig. 16b, with 2 representing some new setting,

$$x_2 - y_2 = a + k$$
$$s_2 = c - k - j$$

and $$r_2 - z_2 = b + j$$

or $$mf_1(u_2) - mf_2(v_2) = a + k \quad \cdots \cdots \quad (14a)$$
$$mf_5(p_2) = c - k - j \quad \cdots \quad (14b)$$

and $$mf_4(n_2) - mf_3(w_2) = b + j \quad \cdots \cdots \quad (14c)$$

Eliminate j and k by the addition of Eqs. (14a), (14b), and (14c); and

$$mf_1(u) - mf_2(v) + \overline{mf_5(p)} - mf_3(w) + mf_4(n) = a + b + c,$$

or $$f_1(u) - f_2(v) + f_5(p) - f_3(w) + f_4(n) = \frac{a + b + c}{m} \quad (15)$$

Any equation involving five variables that can be written in this form may be solved on a special slide rule like the one shown in Fig. 16.   The actual design of the rule, including the layout of the scales and the location of the arrow, is so nearly like the design of the rules explained in previous sections that no example will be given.

(b) Equations containing *six* instead of *five* variables may also be solved on a rule made up of two stationary scales and two sliding scales.   The arrow of Fig. 16 is replaced by a graphical scale in Fig. 17. The new scale is for the variable q, with the equation, $t = mf_6(q)$. By the same methods used several times in preceding sections, the student

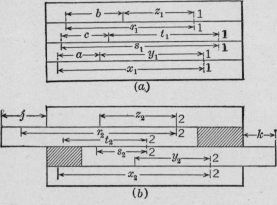

FIG. 17. Slide rule with two stationary scales and two slides (six variables).

may prove that a slide rule, designed as shown in Fig. 17, will solve an equation of the form

$$f_1(u) - f_2(v) + f_5(p) - f_6(q) + f_4(n) - f_3(w) = \frac{a+b+c}{m} \quad (16)$$

14. *Exercises.* Design slide rules to solve the following formulas:

(1) $w_A = 11.5w_C + 34.5w_H - 4.31w_O + 4.31w_S$; the weight of air just sufficient to burn 1 lb. of fuel, w_A, in pounds (8 to 16); the weight of carbon in 1 lb. of fuel, w_C, in pounds (0.4 to 0.9); the weight of hydrogen in 1 lb. of fuel, w_H, in pounds (0 to 0.15); the weight of oxygen in 1 lb. of fuel, w_O, in pounds (0 to 0.4); the weight of sulphur in 1 lb. of fuel, w_S, in pounds (0 to 0.05).

(2) $\dfrac{q}{A} = \dfrac{C\Delta t^{1.266}}{D^{0.2}(t + 460)^{0.181}}$; the rate of heat transfer by free con-

vection, $\dfrac{q}{A}$, in B.t.u. per hour per square foot of surface (50 to 500); the temperature excess of surface over ambient, Δt, in degrees Fahrenheit (10 to 500); the diameter of surface, if cylindrical or spherical, or the vertical height of surface, if plane, D, in inches

(1 to 24); the average of the surface and ambient temperatures, t, in degrees Fahrenheit (100 to 500); a constant depending upon the shape of the surface, C, and having the following values: horizontal pipes, 1.016; vertical pipes, 1.235; vertical plates, 1.394; horizontal plates facing downward, 0.89; horizontal plates facing upward, 1.79; spheres, 1.82.

$$(3)\quad D = \frac{K}{\sqrt{N}} \sqrt[4]{\frac{\text{B.H.P.}}{V}}\;;\quad \text{the diameter of an aeroplane propeller,}$$

D, in feet (4 to 10); the engine speed, N, in r.p.m. (1200 to 4000); the brake horsepower of the engine, B.H.P. (40 to 1000); the air speed, V, in miles per hour (60 to 400); a constant depending upon the number of blades and the setting, K, with the following values: 2 blades — speed setting, 280; service, 300; climb, 315; 3 blades — speed setting, 260; service, 290; climb, 300.

$$(4)\quad P = \frac{p_m l d^2 n N}{1,008,400}\;;\quad \text{the horsepower of a four-cycle engine, } P$$

(10 to 300); the mean effective pressure, p_m, in pounds per square inch (10 to 250); the length of stroke, l, in inches (2 to 8 by steps of $\frac{1}{8}$ in.); the bore, d, in inches (2 to 6 by steps of $\frac{1}{8}$ in.); the number of cylinders, n (1 to 16); the engine speed, N, in r.p.m. (200 to 5000).

15. Equations containing more than six variables, that can be thrown into the form of addition or subtraction of the functions of the several variables, may be solved on slide rules designed like those already described by increasing the number of scales. The general equations that may be solved on such special slide rules containing more than four scales will not be derived here, but the student may derive the equations by using the same principles that have been employed in the preceding sections.

16. (*a*) If an equation cannot be thrown into such form that the functions of the several variables are added or subtracted by any simple method, such as by writing the equation in logarithmic form, it is frequently possible to introduce auxiliary variables and break up the one equation into several equations, each of which is in such form that a solution by special slide rules of the type already described is possible.

As an illustration, consider the following equation, containing five variables.

$$f_1(u) = \frac{f_2(v)f_3(w)f_4(n)}{f_5(p) + f_4(n)} \quad \ldots \ldots \quad (17)$$

This equation may be broken up in either of two ways; by letting

$$A = f_5(p) + f_4(n) \quad \ldots \ldots \quad (18)$$

then

$$f_1(u) = \frac{f_2(v)f_3(w)f_4(n)}{A} \quad \ldots \ldots \quad (19a)$$

and $\log f_1(u) = \log f_2(v) + \log f_3(w) + \log f_4(n) - \log A$ (19b)

Equations (18) and (19b) are then in the proper form for solution by methods used before. Note that the disadvantages of this arrangement are that two graphical scales must be constructed and used for the one primary variable, n, and also that two scales must be drawn for the auxiliary variable, A, one of which is uniform and the other logarithmic.

As a second method, rewrite Eq. (17)

$$f_1(u) = \frac{f_2(v)f_3(w)}{\dfrac{f_5(p)}{f_4(n)} + 1}$$

Then, let

$$B = \frac{f_5(p)}{f_4(n)} \quad \ldots \ldots \quad (20a)$$

or

$$\log B = \log f_5(p) - \log f_4(n) \quad \ldots \ldots \quad (20b)$$

and

$$f_1(u) = \frac{f_2(v)f_3(w)}{B + 1} \quad \ldots \ldots \quad (21a)$$

or $\quad \log f_1(u) = \log f_2(v) + \log f_3(w) - \log (B + 1)$. (21b)

Now, Eqs. (20b) and (21b) are in the desired form. This arrangement is superior to the first because only one scale is necessary for the primary variable, n; although two scales are necessary for the auxiliary variable, B, the transfer from a scale for $\log B$ to a scale for $\log (B + 1)$ is easily made by

drawing diagonal lines between the two scales to connect
corresponding values of B.[1]

(b) As a specific example of the use of an auxiliary
variable and transfer scales, a slide rule is designed to solve
the equation:

$$L = 10,190 \, C \, \frac{CO}{CO_2 + CO}$$

where L = the loss due to incomplete combustion of carbon,
in B.t.u. per pound of fuel,

C = the weight of carbon burned per pound of fuel,
in pounds,

CO = the per cent by volume of carbon monoxide in the
products of combustion,

CO_2 = the per cent by volume of carbon dioxide in the
products of combustion.

Introduce an auxiliary variable and rewrite; let

$$B = \frac{CO_2}{CO},$$

or $$\log B = \log CO_2 - \log CO$$

then $$\log L = \log 10,190 + \log C - \log (B + 1)$$

The accompanying table shows the calculations in the
design of the rule, and the slide rule is shown in Fig. 18.

Variable	Limits of the variable	Function of the variable	Range of the function	Modulus	Equation of the scale
CO_2	6 to 18	$\log CO_2$	0.477	5	$5 \log CO_2$
CO	0.1 to 2.0	$\log CO$	1.301	5	$5 \log CO$
B	3 to 180	$\log B$	1.778	5	$5 \log B$
C	0.4 to 1.0	$\log C$	0.398	5	$5 \log C$
L	20 to 2000	$\log L$	2.000	5	$5 \log L$
B	3 to 180	$\log (B + 1)$	1.656	5	$5 \log (B + 1)$

[1] See "Special Slide Rules" by J. N. Arnold, Extension Series Bulletin 32,
Purdue University.

There are two sliding scales and three stationary scales in this design. In effect, two slides rule are laid out with a common middle stationary support. The lower slide rule solves the equation $B = \dfrac{CO_2}{CO}$; the upper rule solves the equation, $L = \dfrac{10{,}190\,C}{B + 1}$. On the middle support there are two scales for the auxiliary variable, B, the equation of the lower scale being $5 \log B$, and of the upper scale, $5 \log (B + 1)$; no values of the auxiliary variable, B, appear on these scales, but the strokes representing equal values of B are connected by diagonal lines. To use the rule, the value of CO is set over the value of CO_2, and the value of B appearing above the lower arrow is noted; the arrow on the upper sliding scale is then set over the same value of B along the upper edge of the middle support, and the value of L is read under the value of C. For example, as drawn, the rule solves the given equation for the case where CO = 0.2, CO_2 = 6, and C = 0.4, giving the answer, $L = 130$.

(c) One sliding scale and the middle support of the slide rule shown in Fig. 18 may be eliminated by placing the two scales for $\log B$ and $\log (B + 1)$ in the groove. A slide rule with one sliding scale and two stationary scales, like the one shown in Fig. 19, solves the same equation. The left edge of the sliding scale is used as an index in place of the arrows; with this modification, this rule is a combination of two rules of the type explained in Sect. 8, and the principles of the design are the same. To use this rule, the value of CO is set over the value of CO_2, and the position of the left end of the slide on the lower scale in the groove is noted; the slide is then moved to the right until the edge coincides with the corresponding value on the upper scale of the groove, and the value of L is then read directly below the value of C. For example, in the setting shown, CO = 1.0 is set over CO_2 = 10, the left edge of the slide then coincides with a value of 10 of the auxiliary variable, B; before reading L, the slide would be moved to the right until a

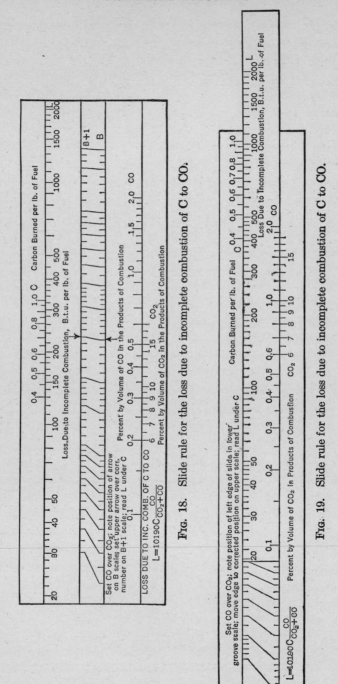

FIG. 18. Slide rule for the loss due to incomplete combustion of C to CO.

FIG. 19. Slide rule for the loss due to incomplete combustion of C to CO.

value of $B = 10$ on the upper side of the groove coincided with the left edge of the slide, when, for $C = 0.4$, L would be found equal to 370.

There is a greater chance of error in using slide rules on which two scales for the same variable must be shown instead of one scale for each variable. For this reason, although many equations can be solved by the methods explained in this section, another form of graphical solution may be preferred.

17. *Exercises.* Design slide rules to solve the following equations:

(1) $Q = 240A \left(\dfrac{t_s - t_r}{215 - 70} \right)^{1.3}$; the quantity of heat transferred from a radiator, Q, in B.t.u. per hour (700 to 86,000); the rated surface for direct radiation, A, in square feet (10 to 250); the temperature of the steam or hot water, t_s, in degrees Fahrenheit (150 to 240); the temperature of the room, t_r, in degrees Fahrenheit (50 to 90).

(2) $Q = 3.33H^{\frac{3}{2}}(b - 0.2H)$; the Francis formula for the flow of water over a rectangular weir with two end contractions, Q, in cubic feet per second (0.1 to 10); the head on the weir, H, in feet (0.5 to 4.0); the breadth of the weir crest, b, in feet (1 to 10).

(3) $\dfrac{T_1}{T_2} = 10^{0.0076fa}$; the tension in the slack side of a belt, T_2, in pounds per inch of width (10 to 100); the tension in the tight side, T_1, in pounds per inch of width (50 to 150); the coefficient of friction, f (0.2 to 0.55); the arc of contact, a, in degrees (100 to 300).

(4) $X = 2\pi fL \left(0.000741 \log \dfrac{S}{r} + 0.0000805 \right)$; the inductive reactance of a transmission line to neutral, X, in ohms (1 to 50); the frequency, f, in cycles per second (show 25, 50, and 60); the length of the line, L, in miles (1 to 50); the equivalent spacing to neutral, S, in inches (50 to 250); the radius of the conductor, r, in inches (0.15 to 0.6, but show the final scale marked with wire gage numbers).

(5) $\dfrac{p_1}{p_2} = \left(\dfrac{t_1 + 460}{t_2 + 460} \right)^{n/n-1}$. HINT: Solve $\dfrac{p}{(t + 460)^{n/n-1}} = A$; the

pressure of a gas during a polytropic process, p, in pounds per square inch absolute (10 to 500); the temperature of the gas, t, in degrees Fahrenheit (0 to 1000); the exponent of the process, n (1.1 to 1.5)

CHAPTER III

NETWORK OR INTERSECTION CHARTS

18. A *network* or *intersection chart* is a graphical representation of an equation containing three or more variables. Graphical scales for each of two variables may be constructed along lines at any angle to each other, and on the coordinate system so formed, lines may be drawn to represent constant values of a third (fourth, etc.) variable. If the two scales are arranged at right angles the coordinate system is rectangular, and this arrangement is most common.

Network charts may be designed to represent all the equations that can be solved on a special-purpose slide rule or on an alignment chart, and they may be used to represent some equations that cannot be satisfactorily solved by these latter means. Also the general form of the relation between several variables is more readily grasped by the engineer from an examination of a network chart than from the study of either a slide rule or an alignment chart.

19. (a) Equations involving three variables, u, v, and w, of the form, $w = f(u, v)$, may be readily solved by means of a network or intersection chart. As an example, consider the representation of the following equation for the density of dry air:

$$\delta = \frac{p}{0.753(t + 460)}$$

where　δ = the density of the dry air, in pounds per cubic foot,

p = the partial pressure of the dry air, in inches of mercury, absolute,

t = the temperature of the dry air, in degrees Fahrenheit.

The network chart to solve this equation may be constructed in many different ways, several of which will be considered. First there is a choice of scales; i.e., either uniform scales or logarithmic scales may be used. Second, there is a choice as to which variables shall be plotted as ordinate and abscissa.

If uniform scales are used, the charts may be drawn on printed cross-section paper; the paper that is ruled with 20 divisions to the inch is superior for most engineering purposes. Using such paper, δ might be plotted as ordinate versus t as abscissa, and lines representing constant values of p might be drawn on this coordinate system. However, in this case, these lines would not be straight but hyperbolic, and since straight lines are desirable because of ease of construction and interpolation, this method will not be used. However, δ might be plotted versus p, and lines of constant t would be converging straight lines with slopes dependent upon the value of t represented.

The first step in the construction of the chart is to select suitable moduli for the δ and p scales. If the limiting values of δ to be shown are about 0.03 and 0.10, a modulus of 100 may be used, in which case the equation of the scale on the ordinate axis is $y = 100\delta$. Since the paper is already ruled, all that is necessary is to mark off the scale by representing an increment in δ of 0.01 by 1 in. or 20 divisions. The limiting values of p are 16 and 30, and since the modulus of the abscissa scale does not necessarily equal the modulus of the ordinate scale, a modulus of 0.5 in. may be used, in which case the equation of the abscissa scale is $x = 0.5p$. The straight lines representing the different temperatures to be shown may then be plotted on this rectangular coordinate system either by locating two points on each line or from one point and the slope. For example, the equation of the straight line representing a constant value of t of -60 F. is $\delta = \dfrac{p}{0.753(400)}$. *Note* particularly that although $\dfrac{\Delta\delta}{\Delta p} =$ 0.00332 for $t = -60$ F., the actual linear slope of this straight line is $\dfrac{\Delta y}{\Delta x} = \dfrac{100\Delta\delta}{0.5\Delta p} = 0.664$ in. per in. The straight lines representing other constant temperatures may be similarly drawn from their known equations. As an alternative method of easily locating these lines, note that for any constant value of δ, $\dfrac{\Delta p}{\Delta t} =$ a constant; i.e., equal increments in temperature are represented by equal increments in pressure along a line of constant density. Therefore, if two lines of constant temperature are located, say for $t = -60$ and $t = -40$, the position of the other lines of constant temperature ($t = -20$, $t = 0$, $t = 20$, etc.) may be found by stepping off with dividers the known increments in pressure for a 20-deg. F. increment in temperature along two lines of constant density. Then, with two points on each straight line of constant temperature known these lines may be drawn.

The finished chart is shown in Fig. 20. To use the chart, enter with a given value of p, follow vertically to the proper value of t, interpolating, if necessary, between the lines of constant t, and follow horizontally to the ordinate scale, reading the value of δ.

(b) The same equation for the density of dry air may also be solved on a chart with logarithmic scales. Rewrite this equation in logarithmic form. Then

$$\log \delta = \log p - \log (t + 460) - \log 0.753$$

If $\log \delta$ were plotted against $\log p$, the lines representing constant values of t would be straight and parallel instead of straight and converging as in the previous solution. If the same limiting values of the variables were to be shown on a chart of about the same size as before, the modulus of the logarithmic scale for δ would be about 13 in., and the equation of the ordinate scale, $y = 13 \log \delta$; the modulus of the logarithmic scale for p would be about 25 in., and the equation of this scale would be $x = 25 \log p$.

On this rectangular coordinate system, all lines of constant t

would have a linear slope of $\dfrac{\Delta y}{\Delta x} = \dfrac{13\Delta \ (\log \delta)}{25\Delta \ (\log p)} = \dfrac{13}{25} = 0.52$ in. per in. By locating one point on each temperature line

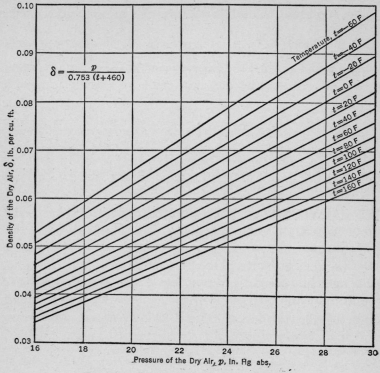

FIG. 20.   Chart for the density of dry air.

shown and using this slope, each line of constant temperature could readily be drawn.

It is desirable to use printed logarithmic cross-section paper whenever this paper is found to have scale moduli that will give a chart of proper size. In some cases, however, such paper is not available, and the scales must be ruled by hand as when making the special-purpose slide rules. The logarithmic scales furnished with the text are useful in constructing logarithmic paper.[1]

[1] Many standard sheets of logarithmic cross-section paper are available in printed form. The following is a partial list of the combinations that may

20. *Exercises.*

(1)–(10), inc.   Solve the problems of the same number in Sect. 10 by means of network charts.

Also, represent the following formulas on network charts:

(11) $d = 1.266 \dfrac{(ab)^{0.6}}{(a+b)^{0.2}}$;   the equivalent diameter, d (6 to 48 in.), of a round air duct to give the same rate of flow and drop in pressure as a rectangular duct with sides a (6 to 48 in.), and b (8 to 72 in.).

(12) $\theta_m = \dfrac{\theta_a - \theta_b}{\ln \dfrac{\theta_a}{\theta_b}}$;   the logarithmic mean temperature difference,

θ_m (5 to 100 F.);   the terminal temperature differences, θ_a and θ_b (5 to 100 F.).

21. (*a*) The network chart is particularly useful in solving two or more equations, each containing three variables, two of which are common, of the general form, $w = f_1(u, v)$, and $n = f_2(u, v)$. To solve these equations, plot one variable, say u, against a second variable, say v, and on this coordinate system draw the curves representing the different constant values of the third and fourth variables, say w and n.

---

be purchased.

$8\frac{1}{2}$ *in. by* 11 *in. sheets:* 1 cycle by 1 cycle, each on 7-in. base; 2 cycles by $2\frac{3}{4}$ cycles, each on $3\frac{3}{4}$-in. base; 2 cycles by 3 cycles, each on 3-in. base; 3 cycles by 5 cycles, each on $1\frac{15}{16}$-in. base; 1.6 cycles (1 to 40) on $4\frac{1}{2}$-in. base by 5 cycles on $1\frac{4}{5}$-in. base.

$10\frac{1}{2}$ *in. by* $12\frac{1}{2}$ *in. sheets:* 2 cycles by 2 cycles, each on 5-in. base.

11 *in. by* $16\frac{1}{2}$ *in. sheets:* 2 cycles by 3 cycles, each on 5-in. base; 3 cycles by 3 cycles, each on 3-in. base; 3 cycles by 5 cycles, each on 3-in. base.

$8\frac{1}{4}$ *in. by* $11\frac{3}{4}$ *in. sheets:* 1.3 cycles (1 to 20) by 2 cycles, each on 125-mm. base; 1.7 cycles (1 to 50) by 2.48 cycles (1 to 300), each on 100-mm. base; 2 cycles by 3 cycles, each on 83.3-mm. base; 2.48 cycles (1 to 300) by 4 cycles, each on 62.5-mm. base.

$11\frac{1}{2}$ *in. by* $11\frac{1}{2}$ *in. sheets:* 4 cycles by 4 cycles, each on 50-mm. base.

11 *in. by* 14 *in. sheets:* 1 cycle by 1 cycle, each on 250-mm. base; 2 cycles by 3 cycles, each on 100-mm. base.

18 *in. by* 23 *in. sheets:* 4 cycles by 5 cycles, each on 100-mm. base.

31 *in. by* 31 *in. sheets:* 1 cycle by 1 cycle, each on 600-mm. base; 2 cycles by 2 cycles, each on 300-mm. base; 3 cycles by 3 cycles, each on 200-mm. base.

Examples of this type of network chart, very commonly used by engineers, are the Mollier and Ellenwood steam charts and the Carrier and Bulkeley psychrometric charts.

(b) As an illustration of the design of a network chart to solve two equations of the above form, consider the solution of the two following equations used in the selection of the proper size of round galvanized-iron air ducts:

$$p = \frac{Q^{1.86}}{5.7d^5}$$

and

$$V = \frac{183.5Q}{d^2}$$

where p = the friction loss in head in round air ducts, in inches of water per 100 ft. of duct,

Q = the rate of flow, in cubic feet per minute,

V = the velocity, in feet per minute,

d = the inside diameter, in inches.

Note that four variables are involved, and that two of these, Q and d, appear in both equations. Rewrite the two equations in logarithmic form:

$$\log p = 1.86 \log Q - 5 \log d - \log 5.7$$

and $\log V = \log 183.5 + \log Q - 2 \log d$

One solution of these equations consists of plotting $\log p$ versus $\log Q$ and drawing on this coordinate system the families of straight lines representing different constant values of d and V. To simplify the discussion the equations are combined and rewritten as follows:

$$\log p = 1.86 \log Q - 5 \log d - \log 5.7$$

and

$$\log p = -0.64 \log Q + 2.5 \log V - \log 5.7 - 2.5 \log 183.5$$

If the range of p to be shown is from 0.01 to 10, a scale modulus of 2 in. may be chosen, and this range will be shown in a distance of 6 in.; the equation of the ordinate scale is $y = 2 \log p$. If the range of Q is from 50 to 300,000, a scale modulus of 2 in. may also be used; the equation of the abscissa scale is $x = 2 \log Q$, and the range of Q will be shown in a distance of 7.56 in.

On the coordinate system selected, lines of constant diameter, d, will be straight and parallel with a linear slope of $\dfrac{\Delta y}{\Delta x} = \dfrac{1.86 \times 2}{2}$, or 1.86 in. per in. Lines of constant velocity, V, will be straight and parallel with a linear slope of $\dfrac{\Delta y}{\Delta x} = -\dfrac{0.64 \times 2}{2} = -0.64$ in. per in. One point on each line that is to be shown may first be located, and the line

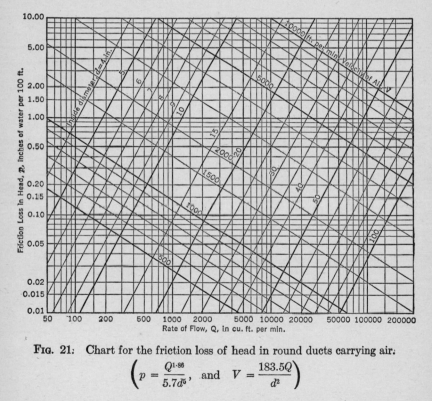

FIG. 21. Chart for the friction loss of head in round ducts carrying air.

$$\left(p = \frac{Q^{1.86}}{5.7d^5}, \quad \text{and} \quad V = \frac{183.5Q}{d^2} \right)$$

may then be drawn through this point with the proper slope. The chart is shown in Fig. 21. With the values of any two of the four variables known, a point may be located

on the chart, and the values of the other two variables may
then be read.

22. *Exercises.* Solve the following equations by means of
network charts:

(1) $p = 0.000822 \dfrac{v^{1.77}}{d^{1.275}}$, and $w = 100d^2v$; the friction drop in
head in hot water pipes, p, in inches per foot (0.001 to 5); velocity
of water, v, in inches per second (4 to 120); rate of flow, w, in pounds
per hour (500 to 500,000); actual inside diameter of pipe, d
(show nominal diameters of standard wrought pipe from $\frac{1}{2}$ to 6 in.).

(2) $p = 0.00145w^2 \left(\dfrac{d + 3.6}{d^6}\right)$, and $w = 0.785d^2v$; the friction loss
of head in low pressure steam piping, p, in ounces per square inch
per 100 ft. of pipe (0.01 to 5); the rate of flow, w, in pounds per
hour (3 to 6000); the velocity of the steam, v, in feet per second
(4 to 80); actual inside diameter of pipe, d (show nominal diameters of standard wrought pipe from $\frac{3}{4}$ to 12 in.).

(3) $$Rp_d = p_w - \frac{(29.92 - p_w)(t_d - t_w)}{2800 - 1.3t_w}$$

and $$w = \frac{0.622Rp_d}{29.92 - Rp_d}$$

the weight of water vapor mixed with 1 lb. of dry air, w, in pounds
(0 to 0.04); the relative humidity as a decimal, R (0 to 1.0); the
dry-bulb temperature, t_d, in degrees Fahrenheit (40 to 120); the
wet-bulb temperature, t_w, in degrees Fahrenheit (40 to 100); the
saturation pressures at the dry-bulb and wet-bulb temperatures, p_d and p_w, respectively, as given in the following table:

t	p	t	p	t	p
40	0.248	70	0.739	100	1.931
50	0.362	80	1.031	110	2.594
60	0.521	90	1.421	120	3.444

HINT: Use w, R, t_d, and t_w as the primary variables and plot w
versus t_d.

23. (a) An equation containing four or more variables, which can be resolved into two or more equations each containing three variables by the introduction of one or more auxiliary variables, may be represented by a network chart.

As a simple illustration of such a network chart, consider the graphical solution of the following equation containing four variables:

$$\text{H.P.} = \frac{2\pi PRN}{33,000} = \frac{PRN}{5252}$$

where H.P. = horsepower,

P = dynamometer load, in pounds,

R = length of dynamometer arm, in feet,

N = engine speed, in r.p.m.

First, the given equation is broken up into two equations of three variables by the introduction of one auxiliary variable, A. By letting

$$A = \frac{PR}{5252}$$

then H.P. = NA

Each of these two equations is then solved by a network chart. To solve the first equation, plot A as ordinate versus P as abscissa on uniform scales, and lines of constant R will be straight and converging. If the limits of P are 0 and 400, and of R, 0 and 3.5, then the maximum and minimum values of A are 0.267 and 0, respectively. The modulus of the P scale may be taken as m_p = 0.025 in., and the modulus of the temporary scale for the auxiliary variable, A, may be m_A = 25 in. The linear slope of any line of constant R may readily be found; for example, with R = 0.5, the slope is $\frac{\Delta y}{\Delta x} = \frac{0.5 m_A}{5252 m_p} = \frac{0.5 \times 25}{5252 \times 0.025} = 0.095$ in. per in.

To solve the second equation with a family of straight lines, plot H.P. as abscissa against the auxiliary variable, A, as ordinate, and lines of constant N will be straight and

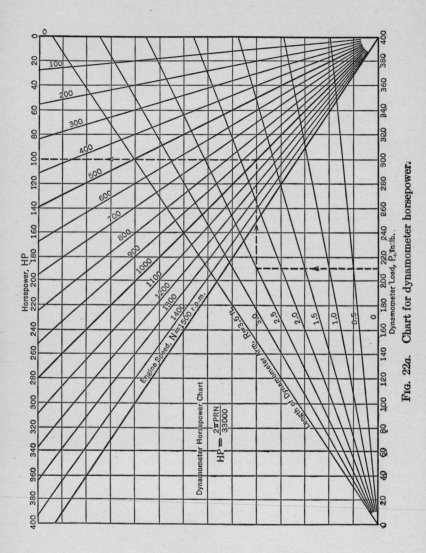

Fig. 22a.   Chart for dynamometer horsepower.

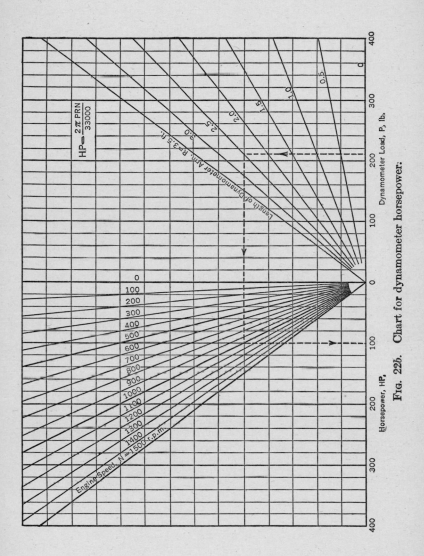

Horsepower, HP,

$$HP = \frac{2\pi \, PRN}{33000}$$

Length of Dynamometer Arm, R = 3.5 ft.

Engine Speed, N = 1500 r.p.m.

Dynamometer Load, P, lb.

FIG. 22b.   Chart for dynamometer horsepower:

converging on this coordinate system. The same scale for A is used in both charts, but there are two different methods of drawing the second chart: by moving the origin to the right and laying out the H.P. scale from right to left, the lines of constant N may be plotted on top of the lines of constant R, as in Fig. 22a; or the scale for H.P. and the lines of constant N may be plotted in a separate quadrant as in Fig. 22b. In either case, the lines of constant N may be located by methods similar to those used above in locating the lines of constant R.

To use either chart, enter with the value of P, go vertically to the given value of R, horizontally to the value of N, and vertically to the H.P. scale. On both charts, the example solved is: $P = 210$, $R = 2.5$, $N = 1000$, and H.P. $= 100$.

As a comparison of the two methods of solution shown in Fig. 22a and b, note that if the curves are plotted on top of one another as in a, greater accuracy is obtained from a chart of given overall dimensions; on the other hand, if there are more than four variables, there may be some confusion and chance for error with so many families of curves plotted together, and the method used in b may be preferred in such cases.

(b) As an illustration of the construction of a network chart to solve an equation containing five variables, consider the solution of Prob. (2) in Sect. 14 with slightly different limiting values of the variables.

Two auxiliary variables E and F, must be introduced in this case.[1]

Let
$$E = \frac{C}{D^{0.2}}$$

or
$$\log E = \log C - 0.2 \log D$$

and let
$$F = \frac{E}{(t + 460)^{0.181}}$$

[1] Note that the number of auxiliary variables equals the number of primary variables minus three.

or $\qquad \log F = \log E - 0.181 \log (t + 460)$

then $\qquad\qquad \dfrac{q}{A} = F \Delta t^{1.266}$

or $\qquad\qquad \log \dfrac{q}{A} = \log F + 1.266 \log \Delta t$

The first logarithmic equation may be solved by plotting $\log E$ versus $\log D$; on this coordinate system, lines of constant C will be straight and parallel with a negative slope. If $\log E$ is next plotted versus $\log F$, lines of constant t will be straight and parallel with a positive slope. Then, with $\log \dfrac{q}{A}$ plotted versus $\log F$, the lines of constant Δt will be straight and parallel with a positive slope. Note that, if the families of lines are plotted on top of each other, there will be danger of some confusion between the lines of constant Δt and constant t unless the numerical values of their linear slopes are quite different.

On the assumption that the final chart is to be shown on 8 in. by $10\frac{1}{2}$ in. paper, the limiting values of the variables, the scale moduli, and the linear slopes of the different families of straight lines are given in the table on p. 49.

The chart is shown in Fig. 23; the logarithmic scales for D on a 5-in. base and for $\dfrac{q}{A}$ on a 10-in. base are the only scales appearing on the final chart. One point on each line of constant C, t, and Δt must be located before these lines can be drawn with the known slope. It is unnecessary to plot temporary scales for the auxiliary variables, E and F, provided the point representing one value of each of these variables is located. For example, suppose that the location of one point on the line, $C = 0.89$, is desired; note at the start that the only scale on the chart is for D. With $C = 0.89$ and $D = 1$, $E = 0.89$, and $\log E = -0.05$. The point representing this value of E is $15(-0.05)$ or -0.75 in. from the origin of the E scale. If the origin of the E scale

($E = 1$) is located, this point can be plotted without a
complete scale for E; from a consideration of the range of

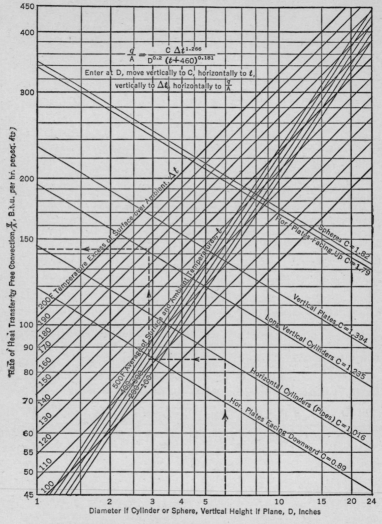

$$\frac{q}{A} = \frac{C \, \Delta t^{1.266}}{D^{0.2} \, (t+460)^{0.181}}$$

Enter at D, move vertically to C, horizontally to t,
vertically to Δt, horizontally to $\frac{q}{A}$

FIG. 23. Chart for the rate of heat transfer by free convection.

E and the space available, we may decide to locate a value
of $E = 1$ five inches above the base line, then the point
representing $C = 0.89$ is 0.75 in. below this point along a

Variable	Limits of the variable	Function of the variable	Range of the function	Modulus	Equation of the scale
D	1 to 24	$\log D$	1.380	$m_D = 5''$	$5 \log D$
E	0.47 to 1.82	$\log E$	0.586	$m_E = 15''$	$15 \log E$
F	0.136 to 0.579	$\log F$	0.629	$m_F = 10''$	$10 \log F$
$\dfrac{q}{A}$	46.3 to 474	$\log \dfrac{q}{A}$	1.010	$m_{\frac{q}{A}} = 10''$	$10 \log \dfrac{q}{A}$

Variable	Limits of the variable	Linear slope of the lines representing constant values of the variable
C	0.89 to 1.82	$-0.2(\tfrac{1.5}{5}) = -0.6$ in. per in.
t	100 to 500	$1.0(\tfrac{1.5}{1.0}) = 1.5$ in. per in.
Δt	100 to 200	$1.0(\tfrac{1.0}{1.0}) = 1.0$ in. per in.

line of $D = 1$. The line for $C = 0.89$ may be drawn through this point with a linear slope of -0.6 in. per in. Other lines may be similarly located.

In Fig. 23, the origin of the logarithmic scale for the auxiliary variable, F, is 9 in. to the right of $D = 1$. Although this origin ($F = 1$) is off the paper, the necessary values of F, from $F = 0.136$ to $F = 0.579$, fall on the paper.

24. *Exercises.* Construct network charts to solve the equations in the following problems:

(1) Prob. (3) in Sect. 12.
(2) Prob. (1) in Sect. 12.
(3) Prob. (8) in Sect. 12.
(4) Prob. (1) in Sect. 14.
(5) Prob. (4) in Sect. 14.
(6) Prob. (1) in Sect. 17.
(7) Prob. (2) in Sect. 17.
(8) Prob. (3) in Sect. 17.

CHAPTER IV

ALIGNMENT CHARTS

25. An *alignment chart* is the graphical representation of an equation of three variables, $f(u, v, w) = 0$, by means of three graphical scales (not necessarily straight), arranged in such manner that any straight line, called an index line, cuts the scales in values of u, v, and w satisfying the equation. Equations containing more than three variables may also be

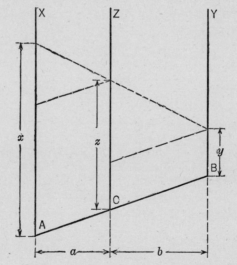

Fig. 24. Alignment chart with three parallel straight scales.

represented by alignment charts with the introduction of auxiliary variables and the construction of auxiliary scales as explained later. Straight-line scales may be used to solve many equations in common use in engineering, although charts with curved scales will also be discussed. In comparison with special slide rules and network charts, the alignment charts are often easier to construct, but they are not completely self-contained; i.e., a straight edge is necessary in their use.

26. (a) The alignment chart with *three parallel straight scales* may be used to represent certain equations containing three variables. In the chart of Fig. 24, AX, BY, and CZ are the three parallel axes, and ACB is the line connecting the origins of the graphical scales on these axes. By similar triangles,

$$\frac{x - z}{a} = \frac{z - y}{b},$$

or
$$bx + ay = (a + b)z \quad . \quad . \quad . \quad . \quad . \quad (22)$$

The axis AX carries a graphical scale for the variable u, BY for the variable v, and CZ for the variable w with the following equations of the scales:

$$x = m_1 f_1(u),$$
$$y = m_2 f_2(v),$$
and
$$z = m_3 f_3(w).$$

Then, substituting in Eq. (22),

$$bm_1 f_1(u) + am_2 f_2(v) = (a + b)m_3 f_3(w) \quad . \quad . \quad (23)$$

This is the general form of the equation that can be represented on the alignment chart with three parallel straight scales; to simplify the construction of the chart, however, let

$$bm_1 = am_2 \quad . \quad . \quad . \quad . \quad . \quad . \quad . \quad (24a)$$

or
$$\frac{b}{a + b} = \frac{m_2}{m_1 + m_2} \quad . \quad . \quad . \quad . \quad . \quad (24b)$$

Then
$$f_1(u) + f_2(v) = \frac{a + b}{bm_1} m_3 f_3(w) \quad . \quad . \quad . \quad (25)$$

Also, let
$$\frac{a + b}{bm_1} m_3 = 1,$$

or
$$m_3 = \frac{b}{a + b} m_1 = \frac{m_2 m_1}{m_1 + m_2} \quad . \quad . \quad . \quad (26)$$

With the assumptions made in Eqs. (24) and (26), the form of the equation that may be solved on the alignment chart with three parallel scales becomes

$$f_1(u) + f_2(v) = f_3(w) \quad \ldots \ldots \quad (27)$$

The steps in the construction of the alignment chart to solve this equation are:

1. Select suitable moduli, m_1 and m_2, for the u and v scales; and construct these scales at any convenient distance apart, thereby fixing $(a + b)$.

2. Calculate the modulus of the w scale from Eq. (26).

3. Locate the w axis from Eq. (24b).

4. Locate a point on the w scale representing a given value of w, and complete the scale on this axis. This last step may be done in either of two ways: given values of u and v may be connected by a straight line, and the intersection of this index line with the w axis represents the value of w determined by these values of u and v in Eq. (27); or the origin of the w scale may be located, since it is on the straight line joining the origins of the u and v scales. Frequently, however, the origin of the scale will not be on the paper, so the first method is often preferred.

(b) As an illustration of the construction of such an alignment chart, consider the solution of the Francis formula for the rate of discharge over a rectangular suppressed weir:

$$Q = 3.33bH^{1.5}$$

where Q = the rate of discharge, in cubic feet per second,
   b = the width of the crest of the weir, in feet,
   H = the head on the weir, in feet.

Rewrite the equation in logarithmic form, and the similarity to Eq. (27) is apparent.

$$\log Q - \log 3.33 = \log b + 1.5 \log H$$

The selection of the moduli and the equations of the three scales are shown in the accompanying table on the assumption that the chart is to be shown on 8 in. by $10\frac{1}{2}$ in. paper.

Variable	Limits of the variable	Function of the variable	Range of the function	Modulus	Equation of the scale
b	1 to 10	$\log b$	1.00	$m_1 = 6$	$x = 6 \log b$
H	0.2 to 2	$1.5 \log H$	1.50	$m_2 = 4$	$y = 6 \log H$
Q	.	$\log \dfrac{Q}{3.33}$		$m_3 = \dfrac{6 \times 4}{10} = 2.4$	$z = 2.4 \log \dfrac{Q}{3.33}$

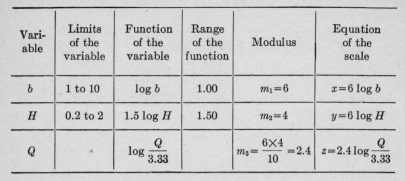

$$Q = 3.33\, b\, H^{1.5}$$

Connect b and H by a straight line, read Q

Ex. $b=1$; $H=1$; $Q=3.33$

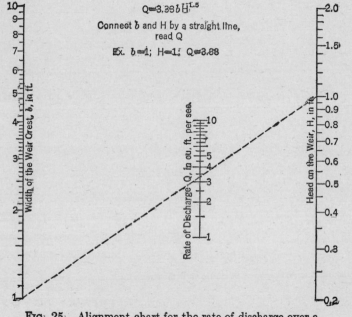

FIG. 25. Alignment chart for the rate of discharge over a rectangular suppressed weir.

Logarithmic scales on a 6-in. base are used for both b and H; the scale for Q is logarithmic with a 2.4-in. base. The b and H scales may be located at any convenient distance apart, in this case, 6 in. Then from Eq. (24b), the location of the Q scale is found to be $\frac{4}{10}(6)$ or 2.4 in. to the left of the H scale. In order to scale the Q axis, connect $b = 1$ with $H = 1$ by a straight line; the intersection of this line with the Q axis locates $Q = 3.33$, which is $2.4 \log 3.33$ or 1.25 in. above a value of $Q = 1.0$. With one point located, the remainder of the scale may be drawn. The chart is shown in Fig. 25. To use the chart, connect the given values of b and H by a straight line and read Q at the intersection of this index line and the Q scale.

27. *Exercises.* Construct alignment charts with three parallel scales to solve the following equations:

    (1) Prob. (2), Sect. 10.
    (2) Prob. (6), Sect. 10.
    (3) Prob. (3), Sect. 10.
    (4) Prob. (5), Sect. 10.
    (5) Prob. (1), Sect. 10.
    (6) Prob. (8), Sect. 10.
    (7) Prob. (10), Sect. 10.

    (8) $\dfrac{t_d - t_w}{t_d - 7} = 0.323(1 - R) + 0.0976(1 - R)^2$; an empirical equation for the relative humidity, $R(0.1 \text{ to } 1.0)$; the dry-bulb temperature, t_d, in degrees Fahrenheit (60 to 100); the wet-bulb temperature, t_w, in degrees Fahrenheit (40 to 100). HINT:

$$1 - \frac{t_d - t_w}{t_d - 7} = 1 - 0.323(1 - R) - 0.0976(1 - R)^2$$

    (9) $\dfrac{t_s + 460}{t_b + 460} = 0.466x + 0.656$; the boiling temperature of aqua ammonia, t_b, in degrees Fahrenheit (50 to 250); the fraction, by weight, of liquid ammonia in the solution, $x(0.1 \text{ to } 0.6)$; the saturation temperature of anhydrous ammonia vapor corresponding to the pressure of the solution, t_s, in degrees Fahrenheit (do not show t_s on the chart but show a scale for the saturation pressure, p_s, in pounds per square inch absolute (10 to 200), constructed from the following table of the properties of anhydrous ammonia):

p_s	t_s	p_s	t_s	p_s	t_s	p_s	t_s	p_s	t_s
10	−41.3	50	21.7	90	50.5	130	70.5	170	86.3
20	−16.6	60	30.2	100	56.1	140	74.8	180	89.8
30	− 0.6	70	37.7	110	61.2	150	78.8	190	93.1
40	11.7	80	44.4	120	66.0	160	82.6	200	96.3

28. (*a*) An alignment chart consisting of two graphical scales and one fixed point may be used to represent the relation between *two* variables; such a graphical solution is sometimes called a line coordinate chart. In Fig. 24, the parallel axes *AX* and *BY* may again represent graphical scales for the variables *u* and *v*, but the middle axis is replaced by a point at a distance *z* from the line of origins (this distance is measured parallel to the axes); then any straight index line through this fixed point cuts the two scales at values of *u* and *v* satisfying the following equation (see Eq. 23):

$$bm_1f_1(u) + am_2f_2(v) = (a + b)z \quad . \quad . \quad . \quad (28a)$$

Let $a + b = k$; then

$$(k - a)m_1f_1(u) + am_2f_2(v) = kz. \quad . \quad . \quad . \quad (28b)$$

or $\quad\quad f_1(u) + \dfrac{am_2}{(k - a)m_1} f_2(v) = \dfrac{kz}{(k - a)m_1} \quad . \quad . \quad . \quad (28c)$

(*b*) When the equation connecting *u* and *v* is known, the usual method of constructing the chart is to select the moduli, m_1 and m_2, draw the two parallel axes at any convenient distance, *k*, apart, and then locate the fixed point. For example, the relation between *u* and *v* might be of the following form:

$$u = cv^d \quad . \quad . \quad . \quad . \quad . \quad . \quad . \quad . \quad (29a)$$

then $\quad\quad\quad \log u - d \log v = \log c \quad . \quad . \quad . \quad . \quad (29b)$

Compare this equation with Eq. (28*c*) and note that

$$f_1(u) = \log u; \quad f_2(v) = \log v$$

$$\frac{am_2}{(k - a)m_1} = -d; \quad \frac{kz}{(k - a)m_1} = \log c$$

The location of the fixed point is known when *a* and *z* are found, and with m_1, m_2, and *k* selected and *c* and *d* known,

$$a = \frac{k}{1 - \dfrac{m_2}{dm_1}} \quad . \quad . \quad . \quad . \quad . \quad . \quad . \quad . \quad (30)$$

and $$z = \frac{(k - a)m_1 \log c}{k} \quad \cdots \cdots \cdots \quad (31)$$

Parallel line coordinate charts are frequently used to represent the physical properties (viscosity, specific heat, etc.) of several different fluids as a function of some other variable, such as temperature, by locating one fixed point on the chart for each fluid. When the equation is known, the above procedure is followed.

A parallel line coordinate chart may be constructed, however, to replace a rectangular coordinate graph, whenever the data plot as a family of straight lines on the latter graph, without finding the equation that fits each straight line. The procedure in this case is to construct, as parallel scales at any convenient distance apart, the two intersecting scales of the original rectangular coordinate graph. A fixed point may then be located for *each* straight line by connecting any two sets of simultaneous values of the two variables (found from the original graph) by straight index lines; the intersection of these index lines locates the fixed point on the new chart. If the straight lines on the rectangular coordinate graph are parallel, the fixed points on the alignment chart will fall on a straight line parallel to the axes.

(c) A line coordinate chart will now be constructed to solve the following equation for the absolute viscosity of gases:

$$\mu = \mu_{32} \left(\frac{t + 460}{492} \right)^n$$

where μ = the absolute viscosity at any temperature, t, in pounds (mass) per second-foot,

μ_{32} = the absolute viscosity of the gas at 32 F., in pounds (mass) per second-foot,

t = the temperature of the gas, in degrees Fahrenheit,

n = a constant for any one gas.

The values of the constants in this equation are given for several different gases in the accompanying table. If the temperature range covered is from -50 F. to 1000 F., the absolute viscosities of these gases will fall between $0.8(10)^{-5}$ and $3.2(10)^{-5}$ pound (mass) per second-foot.

Gas	μ_{32}	n	$a = \dfrac{3}{1 - \dfrac{1.5}{n}}$
Air................	$1.15(10)^{-5}$	0.754	$-3.03''$
Carbon monoxide.	$1.12(10)^{-5}$	0.74	$-2.92''$
Carbon dioxide ...	$0.921(10)^{-5}$	0.98	$-5.66''$
Nitrogen..........	$1.12(10)^{-5}$	0.74	$-2.92''$
Oxygen..........	$1.26(10)^{-5}$	0.79	$-3.34''$

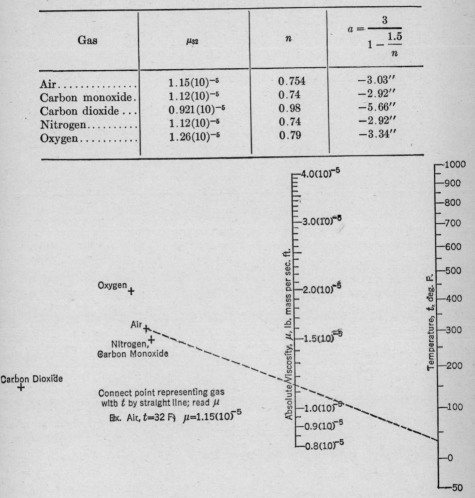

Fig. 26. Line coordinate chart for the viscosity of five gases.

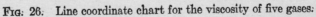

After some preliminary calculations, the modulus (m_1) of the graphical scale for $\log \mu$ has been chosen as 8 in., while the modulus (m_2) of the graphical scale for $\log \left(\dfrac{t + 460}{492} \right)$ is

12 in. The distance between these scales, k, is taken as **3 in.**, and from Eq. (30), a is calculated. (In this example, n corresponds to d in the type equation (29).) The corresponding values of a are shown in the table. Since a is negative the fixed points are to the left of the viscosity scale instead of between the two scales. The fixed points were located on this chart by first connecting $t = 32$ and μ_{32} with a straight index line; the intersection of this line with a straight line parallel to the scales and a inches to the left of the viscosity scale then locates the point for any gas. To calculate z and then locate the fixed point by measurement, as before described, is possible but requires more work in this case. The finished chart is shown in Fig. 26.

29. *Exercises.* Construct line coordinate charts to represent the formulas or data given in the following problems:

(1) $k = k_{32} + a(t - 32)$; the thermal conductivity, k, in B.t.u. foot per hour per square foot per degree Fahrenheit, of some gases and vapors at the temperature, t, in degrees Fahrenheit, where k_{32} and a have the values specified below; show temperatures from -50 F. to 300 F.

Gas or vapor	k_{32}	a
Ammonia................	0.0116	$2.2(10)^{-5}$
Carbon dioxide..........	0.0079	$2.04(10)^{-5}$
Methane.................	0.0170	$3.99(10)^{-5}$
Nitrous oxide...........	0.00796	$0.59(10)^{-5}$

(2) The absolute viscosities of many liquids plot as straight lines against absolute temperature on logarithmic cross-section paper. Draw a line coordinate chart that shows the absolute viscosities of the following liquids. (Show temperatures from -20 F. to 200 F.; i.e., absolute temperatures from 440 F. to 660 F.) The viscosity of each liquid is given at two temperatures.

Liquid	Temperature, deg. F.	Abs. viscosity, lb. (mass) per sec-ft.
Ammonia	−20	$1.55(10)^{-4}$
	40	$0.74(10)^{-4}$
Octane	20	$5.04(10)^{-4}$
	200	$1.78(10)^{-4}$
Sulphur dioxide	−20	$3.53(10)^{-4}$
	100	$1.98(10)^{-4}$
Water	40	$9.41(10)^{-4}$
	200	$1.88(10)^{-4}$

(3) The Prandtl number, Pr, dimensionless, of some liquids is a linear function of absolute temperature on logarithmic cross-section paper. Draw a line coordinate chart that gives the Prandtl number for the following liquids. (Show temperatures from 0 F. to 200 F., i.e., absolute temperatures from 460 F. to 660 F.)

Liquid	Temperature, deg. F.	Prandtl number
Ethyl alcohol	50	18.3
	140	10.0
Octane	50	5.1
	140	4.1
Toluene	50	6.7
	140	4.8
Water	50	9.1
	140	3.25

30. (a) Equations containing four or more variables similar in general form to Eq. (27), i.e., consisting of the algebraic sum of the functions of the variables, may also be represented by alignment charts with parallel straight axes. For example, if the equation to be represented is

$$f_1(u) + f_2(v) + f_4(n) = f_3(w) \quad \dots \quad (32)$$

by letting $\quad\quad\quad A = f_2(v) + f_4(n) \quad \dots \dots \quad (33)$

then $\quad\quad\quad\quad f_1(u) + A = f_3(w) \quad \dots \dots \quad (34)$

By the methods explained in Sect. 26, Eqs. (33) and (34) may be represented by two parallel axis charts with one axis, the A axis, common to both charts. By increasing the number of auxiliary variables and auxiliary axes, equations containing more than four variables may be represented.

(b) As a specific illustration of the above procedure, consider the solution of the following equation containing five variables:

$$w_A = 11.5w_C + 34.5w_H - 4.31w_O + 4.31w_S$$

where $\quad w_A$ = the weight of air just sufficient to burn 1 lb. of fuel, in pounds,

$\quad\quad\quad w_C$ = the weight of carbon in 1 lb. of fuel, in pounds,

$\quad\quad\quad w_H$ = the weight of hydrogen in 1 lb. of fuel, in pounds,

$\quad\quad\quad w_O$ = the weight of oxygen in 1 lb. of fuel, in pounds,

$\quad\quad\quad w_S$ = the weight of sulphur in 1 lb. of fuel, in pounds.

Let $\quad\quad\quad\quad A = 11.5w_C + 34.5w_H$

and $\quad\quad\quad\quad B = A - 4.31w_O$

then $\quad\quad\quad\quad w_A = B + 4.31w_S$

The original equation has been broken up into three equations, each containing three variables, by the introduction of two auxiliary variables, A and B. If the chart is to be drawn on an 8 in. by $10\frac{1}{2}$ in. sheet, the accompanying table shows the scale moduli and the equations of the scales.

Variable	Limits of the variable	Function of the variable	Range of the function	Modulus	Equation of the scale
w_C	0.5 to 0.9	$11.5w_C$	4.60	1.30	$15w_C$
w_H	0 to 0.06	$34.5w_H$	2.07	1.45	$50w_H$
A		A		$\dfrac{1.30\times1.45}{2.75} = 0.685$	$0.685A$
w_O	0 to 0.2	$-4.31w_O$	0.862	5.80	$-25w_O$
B		B		$\dfrac{0.685\times5.80}{6.485} = 0.612$	$0.612B$
w_S	0 to 0.07	$4.31w_S$	0.302	11.60	$50w_S$
w_A		w_A		$\dfrac{0.612\times11.6}{12.212} = 0.581$	$0.581w_A$

The chart is shown in Fig. 27. All the scales are uniform and are located as follows: the scales for w_C and w_H are arbitrarily placed 2.50 in. apart, then the scale for A must be $\dfrac{2.50 \times 1.30}{2.75}$ or 1.18 in. to the right of the scale for w_C; the scales for A and w_O are arbitrarily placed 4.00 in. apart, then the scale for B must be $\dfrac{4.00 \times 0.685}{6.485}$ or 0.42 in. to the right of the scale for A; the scales for B and w_S are located 7.50 in. apart, and the scale for w_A must then be $\dfrac{7.50 \times 0.612}{12.212}$ or 0.38 in. to the right of the scale for B. In order to properly locate the scale on the last axis drawn, that for w_A, values of $w_C = 0.6$ and $w_H = 0$ are connected by a straight index line, thereby locating a point on the A scale; this point is connected in turn with $w_O = 0$ by another index line locating a point on the B scale; this point is connected with $w_S = 0$, and the index line must cut the scale for w_A at a point representing $w_A = 6.9$. With one point on this

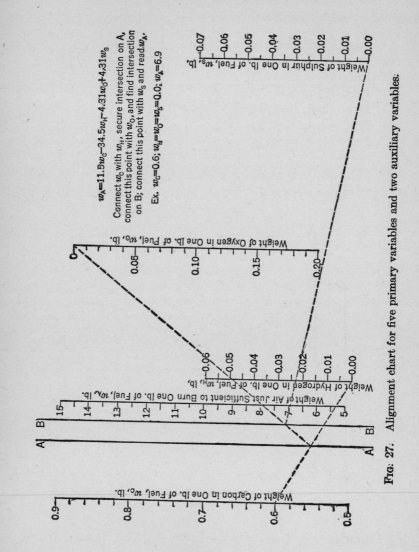

$w_A = 11.5w_C - 34.5w_H - 4.31w_O + 4.31w_S$

Connect w_C with w_H, secure intersection on A, connect this point with w_O, and find intersection on B; connect this point with w_S and read w_A.

Ex. $w_C = 0.6$; $w_H = w_O = w_S = 0.0$; $w_A = 6.9$

Fig. 27.   Alignment chart for five primary variables and two auxiliary variables.

scale known, the remainder of the scale may be plotted from the known equation of the scale.

31. *Exercises.* Construct alignment charts with straight parallel scales to solve the following problems:

(1) Prob. (3) in Sect. 12.
(2) Prob. (1) in Sect. 12.
(3) Prob. (6) in Sect. 12.
(4) Prob. (7) in Sect. 12.
(5) Prob. (2) in Sect. 14.
(6) Prob. (3) in Sect. 14.
(7) Prob. (4) in Sect. 14.

32. The *Z chart* is another form of alignment chart with straight scales that is often used in the solution of engineer-

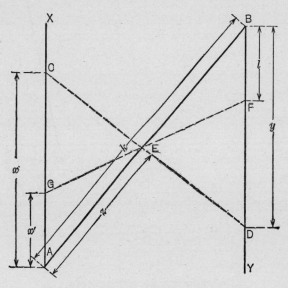

Fig. 28. Alignment chart of the Z type.

ing formulas. A Z chart is shown in Fig. 28; the origins of the two parallel straight axes, AX and BY, are connected by the straight line, AB. The distance between the origins is represented by k, and the dotted index line cuts the axes at C and D and the line of origins at E such that

$$\frac{x}{y} = \frac{z}{k - z} \quad \cdots \cdots \cdots \quad (35)$$

The AX axis carries a graphical scale for u, the BY axis a scale for v, and the AB axis a scale for w with the following equations of the scales:

$$x = m_1 f_1(u)$$
$$y = m_2 f_2(v)$$
and
$$z = m_3 f_3(w)$$

Then, the *general* form of the relation between the three variables, u, v, and w, that may be represented on such a Z chart is

$$\frac{m_1 f_1(u)}{m_2 f_2(v)} = \frac{m_3 f_3(w)}{k - m_3 f_3(w)} \quad \cdots \cdots \quad (36)$$

33. (*a*) One important special form of Eq. (36) is

$$\frac{f_1(u)}{f_2(v)} = f_3(w) \quad \cdots \cdots \cdots \quad (37)$$

This form is readily obtained from Eq. (36) by setting

$$\frac{\dfrac{m_2 m_3}{m_1}}{k - m_3 f_3(w)} = 1 \quad \cdots \cdots \quad (38a)$$

This latter step really determines a special equation of the w scale, for, by substituting $\dfrac{z}{f_3(w)}$ for m_3, Eq. (38a) becomes

$$z = \frac{k m_1 f_3(w)}{m_2 + m_1 f_3(w)} \quad \cdots \cdots \quad (38b)$$

One method of scaling the w axis, then, is to substitute in Eq. (38b) each value of w that is to appear on the finished chart, find z, and plot the scale by direct measurement.

However, there is an alternative method of scaling the w axis that is sometimes easier to use. In Fig. 28, locate a fixed point, F, at any convenient distance, l, from the origin of the v scale on the BY axis; construct a temporary scale on

the AX axis laid off from the origin of the u scale with the
equation, $x' = m_4 f_3(w)$. Connect the fixed point, F, with
the intersection, E, of the first index line, CD. Let the point
G, where the new index line cuts the AX axis, represent the
same value of w as that shown at E.

Then
$$\frac{x}{y} = \frac{x'}{l}$$

or
$$x' = \frac{lx}{y}$$

With the same meanings for x and y as before,

$$x' = l\frac{m_1 f_1(u)}{m_2 f_2(v)} \quad \ldots \ldots \ldots \quad (39)$$

If the modulus of the temporary scale, m_4, is made equal
to $\dfrac{lm_1}{m_2}$, the equation of this scale becomes

$$x' = l\frac{m_1}{m_2}f_3(w). \quad \ldots \ldots \ldots \quad (40)$$

Comparing Eqs. (39) and (40), the equation represented
by this alignment chart is

$$\frac{f_1(u)}{f_2(v)} = f_3(w)$$

Summarizing, this *second* method of scaling the w axis is
to construct a temporary scale for w along the AX axis with
the equation given in Eq. (40); project this scale onto the
AB axis using the fixed point, F, as a focal point, and erase
the temporary scale.

(b) As an illustration of the construction of a Z chart to
represent an equation in the form of Eq. (37), a chart will be
constructed to solve

$$C = 0.000088n(t - t')$$

where C = the correction due to the emergence of the stem
of a glass, mercury-filled thermometer, in degrees Fahrenheit,

n = the number of emergent degrees on the scale,

t = the observed reading, in degrees Fahrenheit,

t' = the temperature of the thermometer stem as read on an auxiliary thermometer, in degrees Fahrenheit.

In Eq. (37), C is the equivalent of $f_1(u)$, $(t - t')$ of $f_2(v)$, and $0.000088n$ of $f_3(w)$. The limits of the variables represented, the scale moduli, and the equations of the scales are shown in the accompanying table.

Variable	Limits of the variable	Function of the variable	Range of the function	Modulus	Equation of the scale
C	0 to 25	C	25	$m_1 = 0.25$	$x = 0.25C$
$t - t'$	0 to 500	$t - t'$	500	$m_2 = 0.01$	$y = 0.01(t - t')$
n Permanent scale	0 to 600	$0.000088n$	0.0528		$z = \dfrac{0.000022kn}{0.01 + 0.000022n}$
n Temporary scale	0 to 600	$0.000088n$	0.0528	$m_4 = 25l$	$x' = 0.0022ln$

The chart is shown in Fig. 29; the C and the $(t - t')$ scales are uniform. The diagonal line of origins may be scaled either by substituting k in the equation for z given in the table and then calculating a value of z for each value of n to be shown, or by projection from a temporary uniform scale. The latter method is shown in this chart. By choosing the distance from the origin of the $(t - t')$ scale to the focal point F as $l = 4.55$ in., the equation of the temporary scale for n becomes $x' = 0.01n$. This scale is readily constructed along the C axis and projected onto the diagonal scale using F as a focal point. The temporary scale has been left on Fig. 29 to show the manner of projection, but this scale is usually erased after projection.

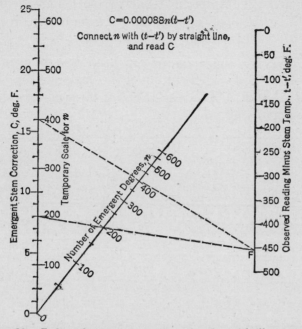

FIG. 29. Z chart for emergent stem correction with illustration of method of scaling the inclined axis.

34. *Exercises.* Construct alignment charts of the Z type to solve the equations given in the following problems:

(1) Prob. (2) in Sect. 10.

(2) Prob. (3) in Sect. 10.

(3) Prob. (4) in Sect. 10.

(4) Prob. (5) in Sect. 10.

(5) Prob. (8) in Sect. 10.

(6) Prob. (10) in Sect. 10.

(7) $\dfrac{t_d - t_w}{t_d - 7} = 0.323(1 - R) + 0.0976(1 - R)^2$; an empirical equation for the relative humidity of the air, R, as a decimal (0.1 to 1.0), from the readings of a sling psychrometer; the dry-bulb temperature, t_d, in degrees Fahrenheit (60 to 100); the wet-bulb depression $(t_d - t_w)$, in degrees Fahrenheit (0 to 40).

(8) Prob. (9) in Sect. 27.

35. (*a*) The general form of the relation between three variables that may be represented by a Z chart, as expressed in Eq. (36), may be rewritten as follows:

$$\frac{m_3}{k}f_3(w) = \frac{f_1(u)}{f_1(u) + \frac{m_2}{m_1}f_2(v)} \quad \ldots \ldots \quad (41a)$$

By letting $a = \frac{m_3}{k}$, and $b = \frac{m_2}{m_1}$, this equation becomes

$$af_3(w) = \frac{f_1(u)}{f_1(u) + bf_2(v)} \quad \ldots \ldots \quad (41b)$$

Note that if a Z chart representing this equation is to be constructed, the modulus m_1 might be chosen first, but the

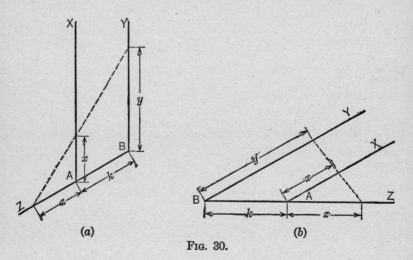

(a)　(b)

Fig. 30.

modulus m_2 would immediately be fixed, since $m_2 = bm_1$. If the modulus m_3 is next selected, the distance along the diagonal line between the origins of the parallel scales would then be fixed since, $k = \frac{m_3}{a}$.

(*b*) If, in Fig. 28, the scale for the variable v is laid off in the opposite direction from the origin B, and if the scale for w is laid off in the opposite direction from A, the resulting alignment chart does not look like a Z on edge but has the appearance of the charts shown in Fig. 30a or b. In Fig. 30,

$$\frac{x}{y} = \frac{z}{k + z} \quad \ldots \ldots \ldots \quad (42)$$

If the axes bear scales such that

$$x = m_1 f_1(u)$$
$$y = m_2 f_2(v)$$

and
$$z = m_3 f_3(w)$$

then
$$\frac{m_1 f_1(u)}{m_2 f_2(v)} = \frac{m_3 f_3(w)}{k + m_3 f_3(w)} \quad \ldots \ldots \quad (43a)$$

or
$$\frac{m_3}{k} f_3(w) = \frac{m_1 f_1(u)}{m_2 f_2(v) - m_1 f_1(u)} \quad \ldots \ldots \quad (43b)$$

Again, by letting $a = \dfrac{m_3}{k}$ and $b = \dfrac{m_2}{m_1}$, this equation becomes

$$af_3(w) = \frac{f_1(u)}{bf_2(v) - f_1(u)} \quad \ldots \ldots \quad (44)$$

(c) As an illustration of the construction of an alignment chart to represent an equation like Eq. (44), a chart will be constructed to solve

$$\frac{E}{100} = \frac{O_2}{0.264 N_2 - O_2}$$

where E = the excess air, in per cent,
          O_2 = the per cent by volume of oxygen in the flue gas,
          N_2 = the per cent by volume of nitrogen in the flue gas.

Comparing this equation with Eq. (44), $a = \frac{1}{100}$, $b = 0.264$, $f_3(w) = E$, $f_1(u) = O_2$, and $f_2(v) = N_2$. The limits of the variables, the moduli, and the equations of the three scales are given in the accompanying table.

Variable	Limits of the variable	Function of the variable	Range of the function	Modulus	Equation of the scale
O_2	0 to 13	O_2	13	$m_1 = 0.5$	$x = 0.5O_2$
N_2	79 to 85	N_2	6	$m_2 = (0.264)(0.5) = 0.132$	$y = 0.132N_2$
E	0 to 150	E	150	$m_3 = 0.05$	$z = 0.05E$

All the scales are uniform; the angle between the oxygen axis and the excess air axis has been made 30 deg. To locate the position of the nitrogen scale, note that $k = \dfrac{m_3}{a} = \dfrac{0.05}{0.01} = 5$ in.; since the origin of the nitrogen scale does not

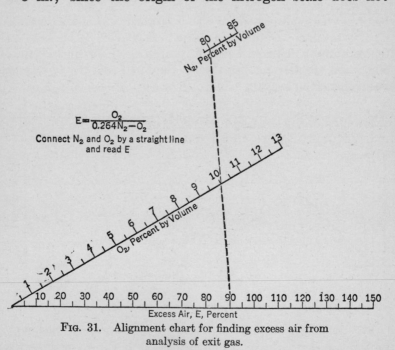

FIG. 31.   Alignment chart for finding excess air from analysis of exit gas.

appear on the paper, however, this scale may be located at a perpendicular distance of 5 sin 30° or 2.5 in. from the oxygen scale. The easiest method of scaling the nitrogen axis is to connect values of E and O_2 by a straight index line and locate the corresponding value of N_2 (e.g., with $E = 90$ and $O_2 = 10$, $N_2 = 80$); the nitrogen scale may then be completed from the equation of the scale. The finished chart is shown in Fig. 31.

36. *Exercises.* Construct alignment charts with uniform scales to solve the following equations:

(1) $w = \dfrac{0.622p}{p_b - p}$; the specific humidity, or the weight of water vapor mixed with each pound of dry air, w, in pounds (0 to 0.1); the partial pressure of the water vapor in the mixture, p, in inches of mercury, absolute (0 to 2); the barometric pressure, p_b, in inches of mercury, absolute (25 to 32).

(2) $Q = \dfrac{2545T_2}{T_1 - T_2}$; the quantity of heat removed from the cold body per horsepower-hour of energy expenditure in the reversed Carnot machine, Q, in B.t.u. (8000 to 43,000); the absolute temperature of the cold body, T_2, in degrees Fahrenheit (440 to 500); the absolute temperature of the hot body, T_1, in degrees Fahrenheit (530 to 580).

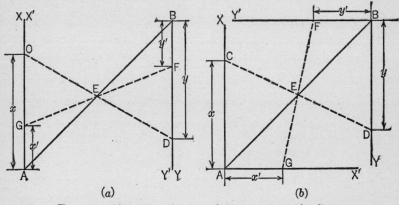

(a)   (b)

FIG. 32. Alignment charts with intersecting index lines.

37. (a) Many equations containing four variables may be represented on two Z charts having a common diagonal line of origins, i.e., intersecting index lines. The chart may be constructed either as in Fig. 32a or as in Fig. 32b. In

Fig. 32a, each parallel axis bears two graphical scales; in Fig. 32b, the axis AX is parallel to the axis BY, and AX' is parallel to BY', and AX' may make any convenient angle with AX.   In either case, AB is the straight line connecting the origins of the scales, and CD and GF are index lines intersecting the diagonal at the same point, E.   In either figure,

$$\frac{x}{y} = \frac{AE}{EB} = \frac{x'}{y'} \quad\dots\dots\dots (45)$$

Let the axes, AX, BY, AX', and BY' carry the respective scales,

$$x = m_1 f_1(u) \qquad\qquad y = m_2 f_2(v)$$
$$x' = m_3 f_3(w) \qquad\qquad y' = m_4 f_4(n)$$

and let
$$\frac{m_1}{m_2} = \frac{m_3}{m_4} \quad\dots\dots\dots\dots (46)$$

The form of the relation between the four variables u, v, w, and n that is represented on such a chart is, then,

$$\frac{f_1(u)}{f_2(v)} = \frac{f_3(w)}{f_4(n)} \quad\dots\dots\dots (47)$$

(b) As an illustration of the construction of a chart to solve an equation in the form of Eq. (47), the following equation may be represented:

$$Q = f(9w_{\mathrm{H}})r$$

where .Q = the quantity of heat given up by the condensation of water vapor in the products of combustion, in B.t.u. per pound of fuel burned,

f = the fractional part of the water vapor formed from the combustion of hydrogen or hydrogen compounds in the fuel that is condensed,

w_{H} = the total weight of hydrogen in 1 lb. of fuel, in pounds,

r = the latent heat of condensation of water vapor at the temperature of the condensation, in B.t.u. per pound of vapor.

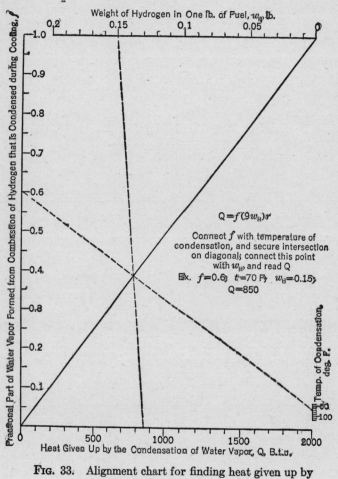

Fig. 33. Alignment chart for finding heat given up by condensation of water vapor.

Rewriting this equation,

$$\frac{f}{\dfrac{1}{r}} = \frac{Q}{9w_H}$$

In this latter form the equation is similar to Eq. (47) with

$$f_1(u) = f, \; f_2(v) = \frac{1}{r}, \; f_3(w) = Q, \; \text{and} \; f_4(n) = 9w_H$$

The limits of the variables, the scale moduli, and the equations of the scales are given in the accompanying table.

Variable	Limits of the variable	Function of the variable	Range of the function	Modulus	Equation of the scale
f	0 to 1.0	f	1.0	$m_1 = 8$	$x = 8f$
r	1069.1 to 1025.1	$\dfrac{1}{r}$	0.00004	$m_2 = 8000$	$y = \dfrac{8000}{r}$
Q	0 to 2000	Q	2000	$m_3 = 0.003$	$x' = 0.003Q$
w_H	0 to 0.2	$9w_H$	1.8	$m_4 = m_3 \dfrac{m_2}{m_1}$ $= 3$	$y' = 27w_H$

The alignment chart with intersecting index lines solving this equation is shown in Fig. 33. The form used is that shown in Fig. 32b; this is superior to Fig. 32a in one important respect, viz., since there are two scales along each axis in Fig. 32a, wrong scales may be connected by the index lines and a large error introduced in the use of the chart. A scale for the temperature of condensation instead of latent heat is shown in the finished chart which eliminates the necessity of consulting steam tables to solve the equation. This scale is constructed from the auxiliary table.

t	r	$y = \dfrac{8000}{r}$
40	1069.1	7.48
50	1063.6	7.52
60	1058.2	7.56
70	1052.7	7.60
80	1047.3	7.64
90	1041.8	7.68
100	1036.3	7.72
110	1030.8	7.76
120	1025.1	7.80

38. *Exercises.* Construct alignment charts with common diagonals and intersecting index lines to solve the following equations:

(1) Prob. (2) in Sect. **12.**
(2) Prob. (4) in Sect. **12.**
(3) Prob. (5) in Sect. **12.**
(4) Prob. (6) in Sect. **12.**

39. (*a*) Alignment charts with two straight parallel scales and one curved scale are useful in solving certain equations containing three variables. In Fig. 34, AX and BY are straight parallel scales and CZ is a curved scale. The index line, DF, cuts the curved scale at E. The straight line, AB, connects the origins of the parallel scales, and the distance between these origins, measured along this line, is k. The lines GE and HF are drawn parallel to AB. Then, from similar triangles,

$$\frac{x - z}{z - y} = \frac{z'}{k - z'} \quad \cdots \cdots \cdots \quad (48a)$$

or

$$x + \frac{z'}{k - z'}y = \frac{k}{k - z'}z \quad \cdots \cdots \quad (48b)$$

The equations of the scales on the axes AX and BY are

$$x = m_1 f_1(u) \quad \text{and} \quad y = m_2 f_2(v)$$

Then if

$$\frac{z'}{k - z'} = \frac{m_1}{m_2} f_3(w). \ldots \ldots \ldots \text{(49)}$$

and

$$\frac{kz}{k - z'} = m_1 f_4(w). \ldots \ldots \ldots \text{(50)}$$

Eq. (48b) becomes

$$m_1 f_1(u) + \frac{m_1}{m_2} f_3(w) m_2 f_2(v) = m_1 f_4(w) \quad . . \quad \text{(51a)}$$

or

$$f_1(u) + f_2(v) f_3(w) = f_4(w) \quad . . . . . \quad \text{(51b)}$$

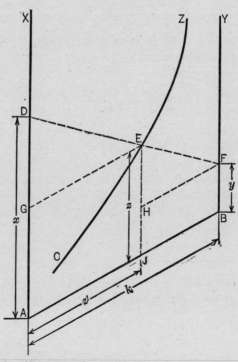

FIG. 34. Alignment chart with two parallel straight scales and one curved scale.

This last equation expresses the relation between the three variables u, v, and w that may be represented on such an alignment chart.

In constructing the chart, the moduli are chosen for the

u and v scales, and these scales are then constructed on the parallel straight axes at any convenient distance apart. To explain the construction of the curved scale, Eqs. (49) and (50) may be solved for z and z' with the following results:

$$z = \frac{m_1 m_2 f_4(w)}{m_2 + m_1 f_3(w)} \cdots \cdots (52)$$

$$z' = \frac{k m_1 f_3(w)}{m_2 + m_1 f_3(w)} \cdots \cdots (53)$$

The position of the curved axis and the scale on this axis are found by substituting in Eqs. (52) and (53) each value of the variable w that is to be represented. For example, with $w = w_1$, find z_1 and z_1', plot along the line of origins, AB, a distance equal to z_1', locating point J_1; from J_1 plot along a line parallel to the AX and BY axes the distance z_1, thereby locating a point on the curved axis representing a value of $w = w_1$.

(b) An alignment chart will now be constructed to solve the Francis formula for the rate of discharge of water over a rectangular weir with two end contractions, an example of Eq. (51b). This formula may be written as

$$Q = 3.33(b - 0.2H)H^{\frac{3}{2}}$$

or

$$-Q + 3.33bH^{\frac{3}{2}} = 0.666H^{\frac{5}{2}}$$

where Q = the rate of discharge, in cubic feet per second,

b = the width of the crest of the weir, in feet,

H = the head over the crest of the weir, in feet.

In the second form, the similarity between this equation and Eq. (51b) is clearly seen, for $f_1(u) = -Q$, $f_2(v) = 3.33b$, $f_3(w) = H^{\frac{3}{2}}$, and $f_4(w) = 0.666H^{\frac{5}{2}}$. The limits of the variables, the scale moduli, and the equations of the two parallel straight scales are given in the accompanying table.

Variable	Limits of the variable	Function of the variable	Range of the function	Modulus	Equation of the scale
Q	0 to 50	$-Q$	50	$m_1 = 0.16$	$x = -0.16Q$
b	0 to 6	$3.33b$	19.98	$m_2 = 0.4$	$y = 1.332b$

Since the Q and b scales plot in opposite directions, the distance between the origins of these scales, measured along the diagonal line connecting them, may be made 10 in., and the chart will fit an 8 in. by $10\frac{1}{2}$ in. sheet. With $k = 10$ in., $m_1 = 0.16$, and $m_2 = 0.4$, Eqs. (52) and (53) become

$$z = \frac{0.042624H^{\frac{5}{2}}}{0.4 + 0.16H^{\frac{3}{2}}}$$

and

$$z' = \frac{1.6H^{\frac{3}{2}}}{0.4 + 0.16H^{\frac{3}{2}}}$$

The calculations of the position of the curved axis and the location of the points representing the different values of H to be shown are given in tabular form. To locate each value of H, measure along the diagonal line of origins a distance

H	z'	z	H	z'	z
0	0.00	0.00	1.1	3.16	0.09
0.1	0.13	0.00	1.2	3.44	0.11
0.2	0.35	0.00	1.3	3.72	0.13
0.3	0.62	0.00	1.4	3.99	0.15
0.4	0.92	0.01	1.5	4.24	0.17
0.5	1.24	0.02	1.6	4.47	0.19
0.6	1.56	0.03	1.7	4.70	0.21
0.7	1.90	0.04	1.8	4.91	0.24
0.8	2.17	0.05	1.9	5.12	0.26
0.9	2.55	0.06	2.0	5.31	0.28
1.0	2.86	0.07			

equal to z' from the origin of the Q scale; then, from this point, measure in the positive direction a distance equal to z parallel to the straight scales. The chart is shown in Fig. 35; note that the first few values of H are directly on

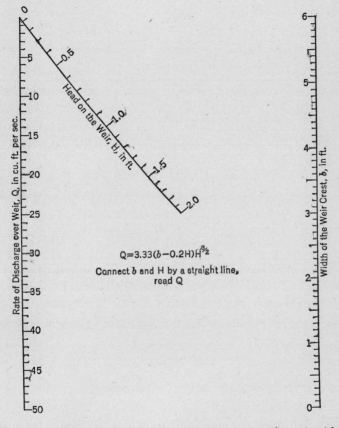

FIG. 35. Alignment chart for discharge over rectangular weir with two end contractions.

the diagonal line of origins, but from $H = 0.4$ on, the points are above this diagonal line and the scale is slightly curved.

40. *Exercises.* Construct alignment charts with two straight scales and one curved scale to solve the following equations:

(1) $V = 0.649\dfrac{T}{p} - \dfrac{22.58}{p^{\frac{3}{4}}}$; the specific volume of superheated steam, V, in cubic feet per pound (2 to 14); the absolute temperature of the steam, T, in degrees Rankine (740 to 1110); the pressure of the steam, p, in pounds per square inch absolute (50 to 250).

(2) $M_e = \frac{1}{2}(M + \sqrt{M^2 + T^2})$; the equivalent bending moment, M_e, in inch-pounds; the applied bending moment, M, in inch-pounds (10,000 to 100,000); the applied twisting moment, T, in inch-pounds (10,000 to 100,000).

(3) $p = p' - 0.011(t - t')\left(\dfrac{1539 + t'}{1571}\right)$; the partial pressure of water vapor in the air, p, in inches of mercury, absolute (0 to 3.5); the wet-bulb depression $(t - t')$, in degrees Fahrenheit (0 to 60); the wet-bulb temperature, t', in degrees Fahrenheit (-20 to 120); the saturation pressure at the wet-bulb temperature, p', in inches of mercury, absolute (a function of t' as given in Sect. 22, Prob. (3), from 40 F. to 120 F. and from -20 F. to 30 F. as below).

t'	p'
-20	0.0126
-10	0.0222
0	0.0383
10	0.0631
20	0.103
30	0.164

41. Alignment charts with one straight scale and two curved scales find some application in the solution of engineering formulas. One arrangement of such a chart is shown in Fig. 36. In this figure, the straight axis AX carries a scale for the variable, u, and the two curved axes carry scales for the variables v and w. The reference line AB is perpendicular to the AX axis at the origin of the u scale; the index line cuts the three scales at points, D, E, and F; the lines EG and FH are parallel to AB. From similar triangles, then,

$$\frac{x-z}{z'} = \frac{z-y}{y'-z'}$$

or
$$xy' + z'y = xz' + zy' \quad . \quad . \quad . \quad . \quad . \quad (54)$$

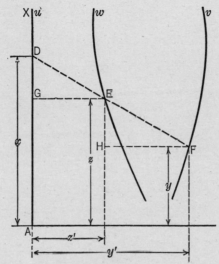

FIG. 36.   Alignment chart with one straight scale and
two curved scales.

For simplicity, let

$$x = m_1 f_1(u)$$

$$z' = \frac{m_2}{f_2(w)}$$

$$z = \frac{m_1 f_3(w)}{f_2(w)}$$

$$y' = \frac{m_2}{f_4(v)}$$

and
$$y = \frac{m_1 f_5(v)}{f_4(v)}.$$

Substituting in Eq. (54),

$$f_1(u) = \frac{f_3(w) - f_5(v)}{f_2(w) - f_4(v)} \quad . \quad . \quad . \quad . \quad . \quad (55)$$

This last equation is one special form of the relation between three variables that may be represented on an alignment chart constructed like Fig. 36. Any one value of w will fix one value of z' and one value of z, thereby locating a point on the curved scale for w; similarly, one value of v locates a point on the curved v scale after y' and y are calculated.

42. *Exercises.* Construct an alignment chart, to solve the equation for logarithmic mean temperature difference,

$$\theta_m = \frac{\theta_a - \theta_b}{\ln \dfrac{\theta_a}{\theta_b}} \; ; \text{ the logarithmic mean temperature difference,}$$

θ_m, in degrees Fahrenheit (5 to 40); the terminal differences in temperature between the hot and cold fluid, θ_a and θ_b, in degrees Fahrenheit (5 to 100).

43. (*a*) All alignment charts with three scales may be quickly reviewed by making use of determinants.

In Fig. 37, the straight index line cuts the scales for u, w, and v in points the coordinates of which are (x_1, y_1) (x_2, y_2) and (x_3, y_3). The equation of this index line in terms of these coordinates is

$$\frac{y_2 - y_1}{x_2 - x_1} = \frac{y_3 - y_1}{x_3 - x_1} \quad \cdots \cdots \quad (56a)$$

or $\quad x_1y_2 + x_2y_3 + x_3y_1 - x_1y_3 - x_2y_1 - x_3y_2 = 0 \quad (56b)$

This equation may be simplified in appearance by writing it symbolically as follows:

$$\begin{vmatrix} x_1 & y_1 & 1 \\ x_2 & y_2 & 1 \\ x_3 & y_3 & 1 \end{vmatrix} = 0 \quad \cdots \cdots \quad (57)$$

This symbolic form of the equation is called a determinant of the third order. The elements in a horizontal line form a *row* and those in a vertical line a *column*. The determinant is *expanded* by rewriting the first two rows immediately under the third and then multiplying the terms along diagonals. The products formed along diagonals sloping down from left to right are given positive signs; those formed along diagonals sloping down from right to left, negative signs. The algebraic summation of these products completes the expansion. The expansion of this determinant results in Eq. (56b), so this determinant is merely a convenient shorthand method of writing the equation of a straight line in terms of the coordinates of three points on the line.

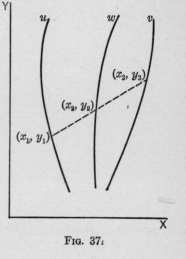

Fig. 37.

(b) In order that the scales for the variables u, v, and w may be represented on single lines, x_1 and y_1 must be functions of u alone, x_2 and y_2 of w alone, and x_3 and y_3 of v alone. Leaving the consideration of scale moduli until later, then, this general condition is met if

$$x_1 = f_1(u) \quad \text{and} \quad y_1 = f_2(u)$$
$$x_2 = f_3(w) \quad \text{and} \quad y_2 = f_4(w)$$
$$x_3 = f_5(v) \quad \text{and} \quad y_3 = f_6(v)$$

The most general form of the relation between u, v, and w that may be represented by an alignment chart with three scales, not necessarily straight, becomes

$$\begin{vmatrix} f_1(u) & f_2(u) & 1 \\ f_3(w) & f_4(w) & 1 \\ f_5(v) & f_6(v) & 1 \end{vmatrix} = 0 \quad \ldots \ldots \quad (58)$$

(c) If any one term in the first two columns of Eq. (58) equals a constant, the alignment chart will have at least one straight scale.   As an example, suppose

$$x_1 = 0 \qquad \text{and} \quad y_1 = f_1(u)$$
$$x_2 = f_2(w) \quad \text{and} \quad y_2 = f_3(w)$$
$$x_3 = f_4(v) \quad \text{and} \quad y_3 = f_5(v)$$

The corresponding chart is shown in Fig. 38 in a general form, and the relation between u, v, and w solvable by such a chart is

$$\begin{vmatrix} 0 & f_1(u) & 1 \\ f_2(w) & f_3(w) & 1 \\ f_4(v) & f_5(v) & 1 \end{vmatrix} = 0 \quad \ldots \ldots \quad (59)$$

Noting that the same subscripts in Eqs. (59) and (55) need not refer to the same functions of the variables v and

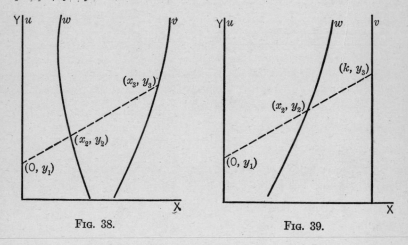

FIG. 38.   FIG. 39.

w, the student may show that Eq. (55) is a special case of Eq. (59).

(d) If any two of the terms in the first column (or second column) in Eq. (58) are constant, then the alignment chart will have two straight parallel scales.   For example, suppose

$$x_1 = 0 \qquad \text{and} \quad y_1 = f_1(u)$$
$$x_2 = f_2(w) \quad \text{and} \quad y_2 = f_3(w)$$
$$x_3 = k \qquad \text{and} \quad y_3 = f_4(v)$$

The relation between u, v, and w that is then represented on a chart like Fig. 39 is

$$\begin{vmatrix} 0 & f_1(u) & 1 \\ f_2(w) & f_3(w) & 1 \\ k & f_4(v) & 1 \end{vmatrix} = 0 \quad \ldots \ldots \text{(60)}$$

After expanding this determinant, the student may demonstrate that Eq. (51b) is a special case of Eq. (60).

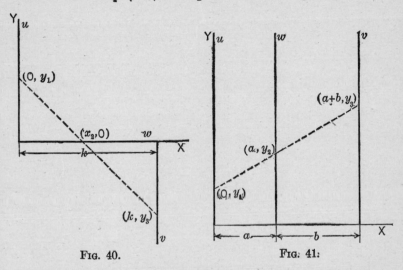

FIG. 40.   FIG. 41.

(e) For simplicity, the Z chart may be represented by two vertical scales and a horizontal line connecting the origins of these scales, as in Fig. 40. The equations of the scales, assuming unit scale moduli, are

$$x_1 = 0 \quad \text{and} \quad y_1 = f_1(u)$$
$$x_2 = f_2(w) \quad \text{and} \quad y_2 = 0$$
$$x_3 = k \quad \text{and} \quad y_3 = -f_3(v)$$

Substituting in Eq. (57), the relation between u, v, and w represented by the Z chart becomes

$$\begin{vmatrix} 0 & f_1(u) & 1 \\ f_2(w) & 0 & 1 \\ k & -f_3(v) & 1 \end{vmatrix} = 0 \quad \ldots \ldots \text{(61)}$$

The determinant may be expanded and compared with Eqs. (37), (41b), and (44).

(f) An alignment chart with three parallel straight scales is shown in Fig. 41. In this figure, if all scale moduli are unity,

$$x_1 = 0 \qquad \text{and} \qquad y_1 = f_1(u)$$
$$x_2 = a \qquad \text{and} \qquad y_2 = f_2(w)$$
$$x_3 = (a + b) \qquad \text{and} \qquad y_3 = f_3(v)$$

The relation between u, v, and w solvable by such a chart is

$$\begin{vmatrix} 0 & f_1(u) & 1 \\ a & f_2(w) & 1 \\ (a + b) & f_3(v) & 1 \end{vmatrix} = 0 \quad \ldots \ldots \quad (62)$$

This determinant may be expanded and compared with Eq. (27).

(g) Alignment charts with the scale modulus of each scale equal to unity are not practical because of awkward shapes and sizes. To make the charts practical, suitable scale moduli must be introduced into the determinants in any specific case. These moduli may be introduced by any method that does not change the value of the determinant. The value of a determinant that is equal to zero is not changed by:

1. Multiplying (or dividing) *all* the terms in a *row* or a *column* by the same number.

2. Changing all the rows of a determinant into corresponding columns.

3. Interchanging two rows or two columns.

4. Multiplying each term of any row or any column by any number and adding each product to the corresponding term of any row or column.

Illustration:

$$\begin{vmatrix} x_1 & y_1 & 1 \\ x_2 & y_2 & 1 \\ x_3 & y_3 & 1 \end{vmatrix} = 0 = \begin{vmatrix} (x_1 + ky_1) & y_1 & 1 \\ (x_2 + ky_2) & y_2 & 1 \\ (x_3 + ky_3) & y_3 & 1 \end{vmatrix}$$

The student may check these rules by expanding the determinant after the change is made.

(h) The example in Sect. 42 will be considered as an illustration of the use of determinants in the design of an alignment chart. The equation given in this example is

$$\theta_m = \frac{\theta_a - \theta_b}{\ln \theta_a - \ln \theta_b}$$

which may be written in determinant form as

$$\begin{vmatrix} \theta_b & \ln \theta_b & 1 \\ \theta_m & 1 & 0 \\ \theta_a & \ln \theta_a & 1 \end{vmatrix} = 0$$

This latter equation is not like Eqs. (58), (59), or (60), and certain changes must be made. First, interchanging the last two columns, the equation becomes

$$\begin{vmatrix} \theta_b & 1 & \ln \theta_b \\ \theta_m & 0 & 1 \\ \theta_a & 1 & \ln \theta_a \end{vmatrix} = 0$$

Then, dividing each term in the first row by $\ln \theta_b$ and each term in the last row by $\ln \theta_a$, the equation takes the general form of (59):

$$\begin{vmatrix} \dfrac{\theta_b}{\ln \theta_b} & \dfrac{1}{\ln \theta_b} & 1 \\ \theta_m & 0 & 1 \\ \dfrac{\theta_a}{\ln \theta_a} & \dfrac{1}{\ln \theta_a} & 1 \end{vmatrix} = 0$$

The next step is to introduce the scale moduli without affecting the value of the determinant. If the chart is to be constructed on an 8 in. by $10\frac{1}{2}$ in. sheet, the maximum allowable value of the short scale (say y) would be about 7 in., while the maximum length of any x scale might be 10 in. With the limits of θ_a, θ_b, and θ_m as given in the problem in Sect. 42, the maximum value of $\dfrac{1}{\ln \theta_b}$ is $\dfrac{1}{\ln 5}$ or 0.621; the modulus for the y scale may be taken as 10 in.   This modulus is introduced by multiplying each term in the second column by 10, which does not change the value of the determinant.

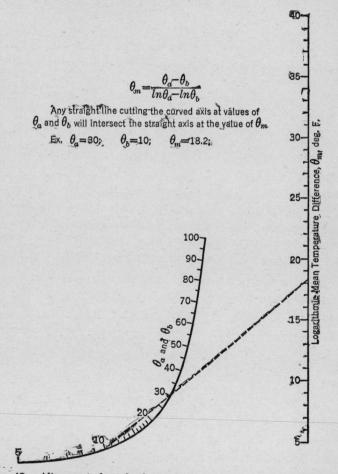

$$\theta_m = \frac{\theta_a - \theta_b}{ln\,\theta_a - ln\,\theta_b}$$

Any straight line cutting the curved axis at values of θ_a and θ_b will intersect the straight axis at the value of θ_m.

Ex. $\theta_a = 30;$ $\theta_b = 10;$ $\theta_m = 18.2;$

Fig. 42:   Alignment chart for logarithmic mean temperature difference:

The maximum value of θ_m to be shown is 40, so a modulus of 0.25 in. may be used on all x scales; this modulus is introduced by multiplying each term in the first column of the determinant by 0.25. The final form of the determinant is

$$\begin{vmatrix} \dfrac{0.25\ \theta_b}{\ln \theta_b} & \dfrac{10}{\ln \theta_b} & 1 \\[2mm] 0.25\ \theta_m & 0 & 1 \\[2mm] \dfrac{0.25\ \theta_a}{\ln \theta_a} & \dfrac{10}{\ln \theta_a} & 1 \end{vmatrix} = 0$$

The equations of the scales are

$$x_1 = \frac{0.25\ \theta_b}{\ln \theta_b} \quad \text{and} \quad y_1 = \frac{10}{\ln \theta_b}$$

$$x_2 = 0.25\ \theta_m \quad \text{and} \quad y_2 = 0$$

$$x_3 = \frac{0.25\ \theta_a}{\ln \theta_a} \quad \text{and} \quad y_3 = \frac{10}{\ln \theta_a}$$

The scales for θ_a and θ_b fall on top of each other, while the scale for θ_m is straight and uniform. In this particular case, the finished chart will have one straight scale and one curved scale as shown in Fig. 42.

44. (*a*) Equations of special form which contain as many as *six* variables may also be represented by alignment charts which use only *one* straight index line for *each* solution. The determinant form of a four-variable equation may be

$$\begin{vmatrix} f_1(u) & f_2(u) & 1 \\ f_3(w) & f_4(w) & 1 \\ f_5(v,p) & f_6(v,p) & 1 \end{vmatrix} = 0 \quad \cdots \cdots \cdots (63)$$

If the student wishes to see this same relationship in a more conventional form, he may expand the determinant with the following result:

$$f_1(u)f_4(w) + f_3(w)f_6(v,p) + f_5(v,p)f_2(u) - f_5(v,p)f_4(w)$$
$$- f_3(w)f_2(u) - f_1(u)f_6(v,p) = 0$$

The graphical solution of this equation is shown in Fig. 43. There are curved scales for the variables u and w, and two families of lines for constant values of v and p forming a network or grid. A straight index line, which connects the given values of u_1 and w_1, is shown; where this line intersects the curve which represents the locus of all points for which the value of v is the given value of v_1, the value of p which satisfies the equation may be found by interpolating between the lines of constant p (in this case, p is between p_3 and p_4).

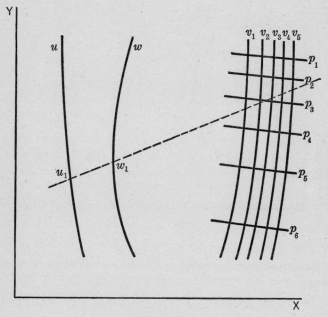

FIG. 43.

(b) Similarly, a determinant form for a five-variable equation which may be represented by one curved scale and two grids, or networks, of two variables each, is

$$\begin{vmatrix} f_1(u) & f_2(u) & 1 \\ f_3(w,q) & f_4(w,q) & 1 \\ f_5(v,p) & f_6(v,p) & 1 \end{vmatrix} = 0 \quad \ldots \ldots \quad (64)$$

The graphical solution of this equation is shown in Fig. 44. The straight index line represents one solution for p (between p_1 and p_2) for the given values u_1, w_1, q_1, and v_1 of the other four variables. Note that any four variables may be given and the fifth found.

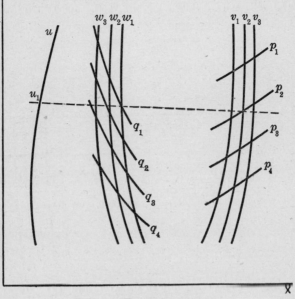

FIG. 44.

(c) The special form of a six-variable equation that may be represented by means of three networks of two variables each, is

$$\begin{vmatrix} f_1(u,r) & f_2(u,r) & 1 \\ f_3(w,q) & f_4(w,q) & 1 \\ f_5(v,p) & f_6(v,p) & 1 \end{vmatrix} = 0 \quad \ldots \ldots \quad (65)$$

The graphical solution of this equation is shown in Fig. 45. By interpolating in the networks, the value of any one variable may be found when the values of the other five variables are given. For the solution shown with the one straight index line, the given values are u_1, r_1, w_1, q_1, and v_1; the value found for p is between p_1 and p_2.

45. (a) In preparing an alignment chart to solve an equation that contains four, five, or six variables, the first step is to form the determinant, if possible, like Eqs. (63), (64), and (65), from the conventional forms of the equations.

First, collect the variables and constants on one side of an equation which is set equal to zero. The determinant may often be formed by inspection or by trial. If this method

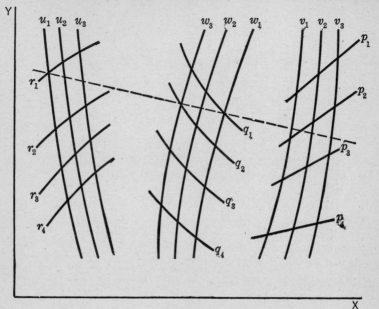

FIG. 45.

is followed, there are no general rules of procedure, except to keep trying. Some will have more success with this method than others.

An aid to the formation of the determinant that is often useful is to break down the original equation into three simultaneous equations, each of the form

$$Ax + By + C = 0$$

A given variable should appear in only one of these equations, and no equation should contain more than two variables.

Then form the determinant from the coefficients of x and y and the remaining terms as follows:

$$\begin{vmatrix} A_1 & B_1 & C_1 \\ A_2 & B_2 & C_2 \\ A_3 & B_3 & C_3 \end{vmatrix} = 0$$

(b) As an illustration of this procedure, consider the following psychrometric formula which contains four primary variables:

$$p = p' - \frac{0.386d(P - p')}{h'}$$

where p = the partial pressure of water vapor in atmospheric air, inches of mercury,

p' = the saturation pressure of water vapor at the wet-bulb temperature, t', inches of mercury,

d = the difference between the dry-bulb temperature and the wet-bulb temperature (wet-bulb depression), degrees Fahrenheit,

P = the atmospheric pressure, inches of mercury,

h' = the latent heat of vaporization of steam at the wet-bulb temperature, t', B.t.u. per pound.

There are four primary variables, p, d, P, and t'. Only one function of each of the three variables, p, d, and P, is involved, but there are two functions of t', namely p' and h', which ordinarily require the use of steam tables or charts to evaluate. Since only two functions of the fourth variable are involved, it seems probable that an alignment chart may be prepared and that it may consist of separate scales for two of the primary variables and a network, or grid, for the other two.

To form a determinant, rewrite the original equation as

$$p - p' + \frac{0.386d(P - p')}{h'} = 0$$

Let $x = p$, or $x + 0 - p = 0$

Let $y = 0.386d$, or $0 + y - 0.386d = 0$

Then $x + y \dfrac{P - p'}{h'} - p' = 0$

From the coefficients of x and y and the remaining terms, form the first determinant,

$$\begin{vmatrix} 1 & 0 & -p \\ 0 & 1 & -0.386d \\ 1 & \dfrac{P - p'}{h'} & -p' \end{vmatrix} = 0$$

At this stage, the determinant should be expanded and checked against the original equation.

The next step is to change the determinant into the form of Eq. (63) by using the rules of Sect. 43(g).

First, multiply each term in the third column by (-1) and transpose columns as follows:

$$\begin{vmatrix} 0 & p & 1 \\ 1 & 0.386d & 0 \\ \dfrac{P - p'}{h'} & p' & 1 \end{vmatrix} = 0$$

Next, multiply all the terms in the first column by 1 and add the products to the corresponding terms in the third column.

$$\begin{vmatrix} 0 & p & 1 \\ 1 & 0.386d & 1 \\ \dfrac{P - p'}{h'} & p' & \dfrac{P - p' + h'}{h'} \end{vmatrix} = 0$$

To obtain 1 in the last term of the third row, divide each term in this row by the last term.

$$\begin{vmatrix} 0 & p & 1 \\ 1 & 0.386d & 1 \\ \dfrac{P - p'}{P - p' + h'} & \dfrac{p'h'}{P - p' + h'} & 1 \end{vmatrix} = 0 \quad . \quad . \quad . \quad (66)$$

It is apparent, now, that this equation may be represented by an alignment chart which will consist of two straight parallel uniform scales for p and d and a network of lines of constant P and t'.

The scale moduli may be selected after arbitrary ranges are assigned the several variables as follows:

Variable	Limits of variable	Function	Minimum value of function	Maximum value of function
p	0–2	p	0	2.00
d	0–40	$0.386d$	0	15.44
P	20–32	$\dfrac{p'h'}{P - p' + h'}$	0.175	1.90
t'	32–100	$\dfrac{P - p'}{P - p' + h'}$	0.0171	0.0287
p'	0.18–1.93			
h'	1076–1037			

The equations for the construction of the chart are:

$$x_1 = 0 \qquad x_2 = m_x \qquad x_3 = m_x \frac{P - p'}{P - p' + h'}$$

$$y_1 = m_y p \qquad y_2 = 0.386 m_y d \qquad y_3 = m_y \frac{p'h'}{P - p' + h'}$$

In the first column of the determinant (the x column), the largest value of a function is 1; the width of the chart will be 7 in. if m_x is 7 in. In the second column of the determinant (the y column), the largest value of a function is 15.44; the length of the longest scale will be 9.26 in. if m_y is 0.6 in. These moduli may be introduced by multiplying all the terms in the first column by 7 and all terms in the second column by 0.6; then

$$x_1 = 0 \qquad x_2 = 7 \qquad x_3 = \frac{7(P - p')}{P - p' + h'}$$

$$y_1 = 0.6p \qquad y_2 = 0.2316d \qquad y_3 = \frac{0.6p'h'}{P - p' + h'}$$

The construction of the network is illustrated by the following example which shows how simultaneous values of x_3 and y_3 are found for a line representing a constant value

P	t'	p'	h'	x_3	y_3
	32	0.1803	1075.8	0.20	0.11
32	40	0.2478	1071.3	0.20	0.14
	50	0.3626	1065.6	0.20	0.21
	60	0.5218	1059.9	0.20	0.30
	70	0.7392	1054.3	0.20	0.43
	80	1.0321	1048.6	0.20	0.60
	90	1.4215	1042.9	0.20	0.83
	100	1.9325	1037.2	0.2 0	1.13

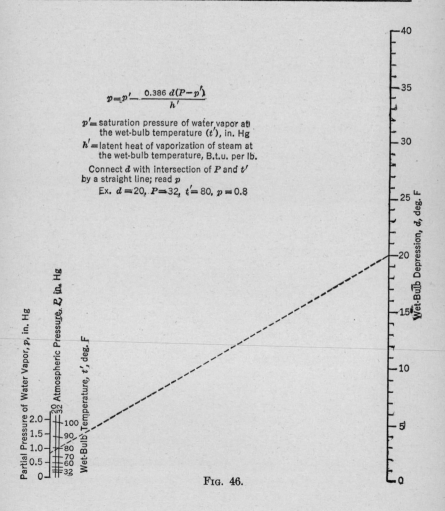

$$p = p' - \frac{0.386\, d(P - p')}{h'}$$

$p' =$ saturation pressure of water vapor at the wet-bulb temperature (t'), in. Hg

$h' =$ latent heat of vaporization of steam at the wet-bulb temperature, B.t.u. per lb.

Connect d with intersection of P and t' by a straight line; read p

Ex. $d = 20$, $P = 32$, $t' = 80$, $p = 0.8$

Fig. 46.

of $P = 32$ and for several different values of the wet-bulb temperatures. The chart is shown in Fig. 46.

46. (*a*) As in the illustrative graphical solution of the preceding section, a chart plotted from the first determinant is often of undesirable proportions and shape. Provided that no single variable appears in more than one row of the first determinant, this determinant may be transformed into a constructional determinant which will give a chart of more desirable shape by a projective transformation. Geometrically, this transformation is accomplished by projecting points from one plane onto another plane by straight lines drawn through a fixed focal point which lies outside of both planes. By such a projective transformation, the projection of any straight line in the original plane becomes a straight line in the plane of projection, while the projection of a curve in the original plane is another curve in the plane of projection.

Mathematically, the projective transformation may be accomplished by multiplying the *fundamental* determinant by a *multiplying* determinant to obtain a *transformed* determinant. The elements of the multiplying determinant, which, unlike the fundamental determinant, is not equal to zero, are the constants

$$\begin{vmatrix} a_1 & b_1 & c_1 \\ a_2 & b_2 & c_2 \\ a_3 & b_3 & c_3 \end{vmatrix} \neq 0 \quad \ldots \ldots \quad (67)$$

In the most general case, the fundamental determinant may be written in terms of six functions (given the sign f) as follows:

$$\begin{vmatrix} f_1 & f_2 & 1 \\ f_3 & f_4 & 1 \\ f_5 & f_6 & 1 \end{vmatrix} = 0 \quad \ldots \ldots \quad (68)$$

The product of the fundamental determinant and the multiplying determinant, which is called the transformed determinant, is

$$\begin{vmatrix} \dfrac{a_1f_1 + b_1f_2 + c_1}{a_3f_1 + b_3f_2 + c_3} & \dfrac{a_2f_1 + b_2f_2 + c_2}{a_3f_1 + b_3f_2 + c_3} & 1 \\[2ex] \dfrac{a_1f_3 + b_1f_4 + c_1}{a_3f_3 + b_3f_4 + c_3} & \dfrac{a_2f_3 + b_2f_4 + c_2}{a_3f_3 + b_3f_4 + c_3} & 1 \\[2ex] \dfrac{a_1f_5 + b_1f_6 + c_1}{a_3f_5 + b_3f_6 + c_3} & \dfrac{a_2f_5 + b_2f_6 + c_2}{a_3f_5 + b_3f_6 + c_3} & 1 \end{vmatrix} = 0 \quad . \ . (69)$$

(b) On the fundamental alignment chart, it is possible to connect the four extreme corners of the chart by straight lines to form a bounding quadrilateral. This bounding quadrilateral will contain the points which represent all values of all the variables that appear on the chart. The projective transformation may be used to transform this quadrilateral which bounds the chart in the original plane into a rectangle of predetermined size which will bound the chart in the plane of the projection. This is accomplished by determining the values of the nine constants in the multiplying determinant.

To illustrate the projective transformation, consider the illustrative example of the preceding section given by Eq. (66) before the introduction of any scale moduli. With the same limits of the variables arbitrarily assigned before, the coordinates of the four corners of the bounding quadrilateral in the fundamental determinant were

$$x_1 = 0 \quad \text{and} \quad y_1 = 0 \qquad (\text{when } p = 0)$$
$$x_2 = 0 \quad \text{and} \quad y_2 = 2 \qquad (\text{when } p = 2)$$
$$x_3 = 1 \quad \text{and} \quad y_3 = 0 \qquad (\text{when } d = 0)$$
$$x_4 = 1 \quad \text{and} \quad y_4 = 15.44 \quad (\text{when } d = 40)$$

Although not essential in the development of the principles of the projective transformation, it may be noted that the introduction of scale moduli in this example changed the coordinates of the four corners of the bounding quadrilaterals to

$$x_1 = 0 \quad \text{and} \quad y_1 = 0 \qquad (\text{when } p = 0)$$
$$x_2 = 0 \quad \text{and} \quad y_2 = 1.2 \qquad (\text{when } p = 2)$$
$$x_3 = 7 \quad \text{and} \quad y_3 = 0 \qquad (\text{when } d = 0)$$
$$x_4 = 7 \quad \text{and} \quad y_4 = 9.26 \qquad (\text{when } d = 40)$$

Assume that it is desired, by projective transformation, to change the bounding quadrilateral of the fundamental chart into a bounding rectangle in the projected chart which will be 7 in. wide by 9 in. high. In other words

$$x_1 = 0 \quad \text{and} \quad y_1 = 0 \quad \text{(when } p = 0)$$
$$x_2 = 0 \quad \text{and} \quad y_2 = 9 \quad \text{(when } p = 2)$$
$$x_3 = 7 \quad \text{and} \quad y_3 = 0 \quad \text{(when } d = 0)$$
$$x_4 = 7 \quad \text{and} \quad y_4 = 9 \quad \text{(when } d = 40)$$

A comparison of the special case (Eq. 66) with the general case of the fundamental determinant (Eq. 68) shows that

$$f_1 = 0 \qquad\qquad f_2 = p$$
$$f_3 = 1 \qquad\qquad f_4 = 0.386d$$
$$f_5 = \frac{P - p'}{P - p' + h'} \qquad f_6 = \frac{p'h'}{P - p' + h'}$$

There are eight equations now available to determine the nine constants of the multiplying determinant. These eight equations define the corners of the limiting rectangle of the projected chart to be constructed from the transformed determinant (Eq. 69):

$$x_1 = 0 \text{ when } p = 0;$$
$$x_1 = \frac{a_1f_1 + b_1f_2 + c_1}{a_3f_1 + b_3f_2 + c_3} = \frac{0 + 0 + c_1}{0 + 0 + c_3} = 0,$$

or
$$\frac{c_1}{c_3} = 0$$

$$y_1 = 0 \text{ when } p = 0;$$
$$y_1 = \frac{a_2f_1 + b_2f_2 + c_2}{a_3f_1 + b_3f_2 + c_3} = \frac{0 + 0 + c_2}{0 + 0 + c_3} = 0,$$

or
$$\frac{c_2}{c_3} = 0$$

$$x_2 = 0 \text{ when } p = 2;$$
$$x_2 = \frac{a_1f_1 + b_1f_2 + c_1}{a_3f_1 + b_3f_2 + c_3} = \frac{0 + 2b_1 + c_1}{0 + 2b_3 + c_3} = 0,$$

or
$$\frac{2b_1 + c_1}{2b_3 + c_3} = 0$$

$y_2 = 9$ when $p = 2$;

$$y_2 = \frac{a_2 f_1 + b_2 f_2 + c_2}{a_3 f_1 + b_3 f_2 + c_3} = \frac{0 + 2b_2 + c_2}{0 + 2b_3 + c_3} = 9,$$

or
$$\frac{2b_2 + c_2}{2b_3 + c_3} = 9$$

$x_3 = 7$ when $d = 0$;

$$x_3 = \frac{a_1 f_3 + b_1 f_4 + c_1}{a_3 f_3 + b_3 f_4 + c_3} = \frac{a_1 + 0 + c_1}{a_3 + 0 + c_3} = 7,$$

or
$$\frac{a_1 + c_1}{a_3 + c_3} = 7$$

$y_3 = 0$ when $d = 0$;

$$y_3 = \frac{a_2 f_3 + b_2 f_4 + c_2}{a_3 f_3 + b_3 f_4 + c_3} = \frac{a_2 + 0 + c_2}{a_3 + 0 + c_3} = 0,$$

or
$$\frac{a_2 + c_2}{a_3 + c_3} = 0$$

$x_4 = 7$ when $d = 40$;

$$x_4 = \frac{a_1 f_3 + b_1 f_4 + c_1}{a_3 f_3 + b_3 f_4 + c_3} = \frac{a_1 + 15.44 b_1 + c_1}{a_3 + 15.44 b_3 + c_3} = 7,$$

or
$$\frac{a_1 + 15.44 b_1 + c_1}{a_3 + 15.44 b_3 + c_3} = 7$$

$y_4 = 9$ when $d = 40$;

$$y_4 = \frac{a_2 f_3 + b_2 f_4 + c_2}{a_3 f_3 + b_3 f_4 + c_3} = \frac{a_2 + 15.44 b_2 + c_2}{a_3 + 15.44 b_3 + c_3} = 9,$$

or
$$\frac{a_2 + 15.44 b_2 + c_2}{a_3 + 15.44 b_3 + c_3} = 9$$

From these eight equations, it may be seen at once that $c_1 = c_2 = b_1 = a_2 = 0$. The remaining four equations are

$$2b_2 - 18b_3 - 9c_3 = 0$$
$$a_1 - 7a_3 - 7c_3 = 0$$
$$a_1 - 7a_3 - 108.08b_3 - 7c_3 = 0$$
$$15.44b_2 - 9a_3 - 138.96b_3 - 9c_3 = 0$$

By inspection of these equations, it is apparent that $b_3 = 0$. In the three remaining equations there are four variables. By assigning an arbitrary value, other than zero, to any one of these variables, the other three may be found. The student may show by trial that the final form of the transformed determinant is independent of the numerical value assigned to this one variable.

In this case, let $c_3 = 1$, then $b_2 = 4.5$, $a_3 = 6.72$, and $a_1 = 54.04$. The multiplying determinant in this example is

$$\begin{vmatrix} 54.04 & 0 & 0 \\ 0 & 4.5 & 0 \\ 6.72 & 0 & 1 \end{vmatrix}$$

The transformed determinant is found by substitution in Eq. (69) to be

$$\begin{vmatrix} 0 & 4.5p & 1 \\ 7 & 0.225d & 1 \\ \dfrac{7(P - p')}{P - p' + 0.1295h'} & \dfrac{0.5829p'h'}{P - p' + 0.1295h'} & 1 \end{vmatrix} = 0$$

The final equations for the construction of the projected chart are

$$x_1 = 0 \qquad x_2 = 7 \qquad x_3 = \frac{7(P - p')}{P - p' + 0.1295h'}$$

$$y_1 = 4.5p \qquad y_2 = 0.225d \qquad y_3 = \frac{0.5829p'h'}{P - p' + 0.1295h'}$$

The projected chart is shown in Fig 47; this chart should be compared with Fig. 46 to see how the shape of the chart has been changed.

47. Many equations containing more than three variables may be represented by a combination of two or more of the various types of alignment charts described in this chapter. Alignment charts and network charts may also be combined. Although combinations of special-purpose slide rules and network or alignment charts are rare, a few solutions may conveniently be represented by a combination of a network chart and a special-purpose slide rule.

The methods of combining these graphical solutions need no explanation other than to say that auxiliary variables and transfer axes are commonly used to tie the two or more charts together. Considerable ingenuity is often required to hit upon the most effective combination.

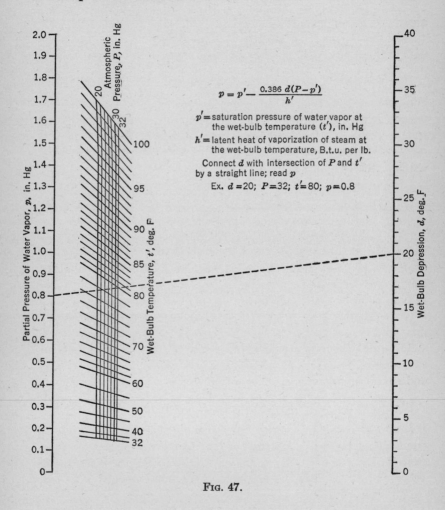

$$p = p' - \frac{0.386\ d(P - p')}{h'}$$

p' = saturation pressure of water vapor at the wet-bulb temperature (t'), in. Hg

h' = latent heat of vaporization of steam at the wet-bulb temperature, B.t.u. per lb.

Connect d with intersection of P and t' by a straight line; read p

Ex. d =20; P=32; t'=80; p=0.8

FIG. 47.

48. *Exercises.* Write the following equations in determinant form, and construct alignment charts to solve the resulting equations:

(1) $Q = 3.33(b - 0.2H)H^{\frac{3}{2}}$; the rate of discharge, Q (0 to 50 cu. ft. per sec.) of a rectangular weir with two end contractions with a width of weir crest, b (0 to 6 ft.), and with a head, H (0 to 2 ft.).

(2) $V = 0.649 \dfrac{T}{p} - \dfrac{22.58}{p^{\frac{5}{4}}}$; the specific volume of superheated steam, V, in cubic feet per pound (2 to 14); the absolute temperature of the steam, T, in degrees Rankine (740 to 1110); the pressure of the steam, p, in pounds per square inch absolute (50 to 250).

(3) $L = 10190$ C $\dfrac{CO}{CO_2 + CO}$; the loss due to incomplete combustion of carbon, L, B.t.u. per pound of fuel (0 to 2600); the weight of carbon burned per pound of fuel, C, pounds (0 to 1.0); the per cent by volume of carbon monoxide in the products of combustion, CO (0 to 2); the per cent by volume of carbon dioxide in the products of combustion, CO_2 (6 to 16).

(4) $C = \dfrac{41.65 + \dfrac{0.00281}{S} + \dfrac{1.811}{n}}{1 + \dfrac{n}{\sqrt{R}}\left(41.65 + \dfrac{0.00281}{S}\right)}$; the Ganguillet and Kutter empirical formula for the Chezy coefficient for flow in open channels, C (0 to 280); the coefficient of roughness, n (0.01 to 0.06); the hydraulic slope, S (0.00002 to 0.01); the hydraulic radius, R, in feet (0.2 to 30).

(5) $w^3 + aw^2 + bw + c = 0$ (the cubic equation with arbitrary limits for a, b, c, and w).

The following equations may be solved by a combination of two alignment charts or by the combination of alignment chart and network chart:

(6) $\dfrac{E}{100} = \dfrac{O_2 - 0.5\,CO}{0.264\,N_2 - (O_2 - 0.5\,CO)}$; the per cent excess air, E (0 to 150); the per cent by volume of oxygen in the products of combustion, O_2 (0 to 15); the per cent by volume of carbon monoxide in the products of combustion, CO (0 to 2); the per cent by volume of nitrogen in the products of combustion, N_2 (79 to 85).

(7) Prob. (1) in Sect. 17.

(8) Prob. (3) in Sect. 17.

(9) Prob. (5) in Sect. 17.

(10) $p = \dfrac{0.054(a + b)Q^{1.86}}{(ab)^3}$; the friction loss in head for the

flow of air of standard density through rectangular ducts, p, inches of water per 100 ft. of duct (0.01 to 10); side of duct, a, inches (4 to 60); side of duct, b, inches (6 to 100); the rate of air flow, Q, cubic feet per minute (50 to 250,000).

CHAPTER V

EMPIRICAL EQUATIONS — NON-PERIODIC CURVES

49. (a) When simultaneous values of two interdependent quantities have been obtained by experiment, the data may be plotted as points on rectangular coordinates. If a smooth curve can be drawn to pass near the plotted points, an approximate relation between the two quantities may be represented mathematically by the equation of this curve. This equation is called an *empirical equation*; i.e., the equation expresses the results of experiment and may or may not be the *rational* expression of a physical, chemical, or biological law.

Such empirical equations are used in computing the value of one of the interdependent quantities when a value of the other is given, provided that these values come within the range of the original experiments. It is exceedingly dangerous, however, to extend the use of the equation beyond the limits of the original observations.

(b) The first step in the determination of the equation is to plot the data on ordinary cross-section paper bearing uniform scales; the second step is to determine the form of the smooth curve fitting these data. The nature of the experiment may suggest the form of this equation; if not, the points may be best fitted by a straight line, a parabola, or by some of the curves discussed later. The third step is to check the choice of curve form by "rectifying" the curve, i.e., usually by replotting the data on a rectangular coordinate system with the two scales chosen as such functions of the variables that the data plot as a straight line. The fourth step is to determine the numerical values of the constants in the equation.

50. (a) Assuming, for the present, that the *form of the equation is known*, there are several methods that may be used in finding the constants. In any case, the number of constants in the equation, the accuracy warranted in their determination, and any known facts that precisely fix one or more points on the curve are important. With n constants in the equation, three methods of determining these constants follow:

1. The method of *selected points*. Select n points nearest to the smooth curve through the data and read the simultaneous values of the two variables. Write the equation connecting these variables n times, substituting in each equation a different pair of simultaneous values. Solve these n equations simultaneously for the values of the n constants.

2. The method of *group averages* by *residual summation*. Divide the experimental data into n groups, taking about the same number of experimental points for each group. Let the vertical distances from the plotted points to the imaginary best curve through these points be called the *residuals*. Write n equations on the assumption that, for each group, the summation of the residuals is zero, and solve these equations simultaneously for the n constants.

3. The method of *least squares*. The best curve through the data is assumed to result when the summation of the squares of the residuals is a minimum. The data need not be broken up into groups, but the partial derivatives of the summation of the squares of the residuals with respect to each of the n constants are equated to zero. These n equations are then solved for the n constants.

(b) The determination of the constants by the method of selected points probably needs no further explanation, but the application of the last two methods will be explained. The latent heat of vaporization of steam, r, is given in the following table at different temperatures, t. For the range of temperatures involved, a straight line of the form, $r = a - bt$, fits the data very well. The two constants, b and a, are to be determined.

	t	r	rt	t^2
	40	1069.1	42,764	1,600
	50	1063.6	53,180	2,500
	60	1058.2	63,492	3,600
	70	1052.7	73,689	4,900
Σ	220	4243.6	233,125	12,600
	80	1047.3	83,784	6,400
	90	1041.8	93,762	8,100
	100	1036.3	103,630	10,000
	110	1030.8	113,388	12,100
Σ	380	4156.2	394,564	36,600
$\Sigma\Sigma$	600	8399.8	627,689	49,200

By the method of *group averages*, the best line through the data is assumed to result when

$$\Sigma r - \Sigma(a - bt) = 0$$

Breaking the data up into two groups, each containing four observations, the following equation may be written for each group:

$$\Sigma r - \Sigma(a - bt) = \Sigma r - 4a + b\Sigma t = 0$$

Substituting the summations of each group,

$$4243.6 - 4a + 220b = 0$$

and $$4156.2 - 4a + 380b = 0$$

Solving simultaneously, we find

$$b = 0.546 \quad \text{and} \quad a = 1090.9$$

The corresponding empirical equation for latent heat in this temperature range becomes,

$$r = 1090.9 - 0.546t$$

Note that by this method slightly different values of the constants may be obtained by a different grouping of the data (i.e., by taking three observations, say, in the first group, and five in the second).

By the method of *least squares*, the best line through the data is assumed to result when

$$\frac{\delta[\sum(r - a + bt)^2]}{\delta a} = -2\sum[(r - a + bt)] = 0$$

and

$$\frac{\delta[\sum(r - a + bt)^2]}{\delta b} = 2\sum[(r - a + bt)(t)] = 0$$

Rewriting these equations for the eight observations

$$-\sum r + 8a - b\sum t = 0$$

and

$$\sum rt - a\sum t + b\sum t^2 = 0$$

Substituting,

$$-8399.8 + 8a - 600b = 0$$

and

$$627,689 - 600a + 49,200b = 0$$

Solving simultaneously, we find

$$b = 0.547 \quad \text{and} \quad a = 1091.0$$

The corresponding empirical equation becomes

$$r = 1091.0 - 0.547t$$

The same values of the constants should be obtained by any student using the method of least squares, because it is not necessary to break the data up into groups. This method gives the most accurate evaluation of the constants, but the accuracy of the data may not always *demand* its use for engineering purposes.

51. (a) In order to assist in recognizing the equation of the curve that best fits the plotted data, several equations containing *two constants* will be given in this section.

Methods of plotting that transform these curves into straight lines will also be considered.

(b) *The straight line, $y = a + bx$.*   In the equation of the straight line, the slope of the line is $b = \dfrac{\Delta y}{\Delta x}$, while the intercept on the Y axis $(x = 0)$ is a.   In Fig. 48 are shown three straight lines together with the equation of each.   One of these lines passes through the origin, and $a = 0$.   Another has a positive slope and a negative intercept, and the third

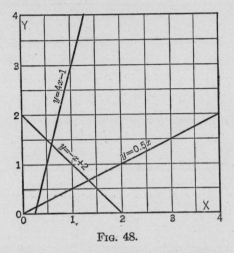

Fig. 48.

has a negative slope and a positive intercept.   An illustration of the method of determining the constants a and b, when a straight line best fits the data, was given in the preceding section.

(c) *Simple parabola or hyperbola, $y = ax^b$.*   This curve is parabolic for positive values of b, and hyperbolic, with the axes as asymptotes, for negative values of b.   If b is greater than 1, the curves are ascending concave; if b is positive but less than 1, the curves are ascending convex; if b is negative the curves are descending concave.[1]

---

[1] These are arbitrary but useful descriptions of curve forms.   To determine whether the curve is *ascending* or *descending*, trace the line in the positive direction of x; the *concavity* or *convexity* refers to the shape of the curved surface bounded by the line and the X and Y axes.

In Fig. 49*a* are shown three curves with the following equations:

$$y = 2x^{0.5}; \quad y = 10x^{-0.8}; \quad \text{and} \quad y = 0.6x^{1.2}$$

To verify whether the data are closely approximated by a curve of the simple parabolic or hyperbolic form, plot log *y* versus log *x*, or plot *y* versus *x* on logarithmic cross-section paper;[1] if a straight line satisfactorily fits the data on this plot, the use of the above general form of the equation is justified.

In Fig. 49*b*, the same three curves are plotted on logarithmic cross-section paper. The parabola becomes a straight line with a positive slope, the hyperbola a straight line with a negative slope. The reason for this is obvious if the logarithmic form of the equation is written:

$$\log y = \log a + b \log x$$

This is an equation of the first degree in log *y* and log *x*, and with these functions as coordinates, the equation plots as a straight line with a slope of $b = \dfrac{\Delta (\log y)}{\Delta (\log x)}$ and an intercept, for $\log x = 0 (x = 1)$, of $\log y = \log a$. The two constants, *a* and *b*, may be determined from the equation of the straight line by one of the methods described in Sect. 50.

(*d*) *Hyperbola*, $y = \dfrac{x}{a + bx}$. This is the equation of an hyperbola with asymptotes $x = -\dfrac{a}{b}$ and $y = \dfrac{1}{b}$. In Fig. 50*a* are shown three curves with the following equations:

$$y = \frac{x}{0.2 + 0.2x}$$

$$y = \frac{x}{-0.1 + 0.2x}$$

$$y = \frac{x}{2 - 0.1x}$$

[1] See Sect. 19.

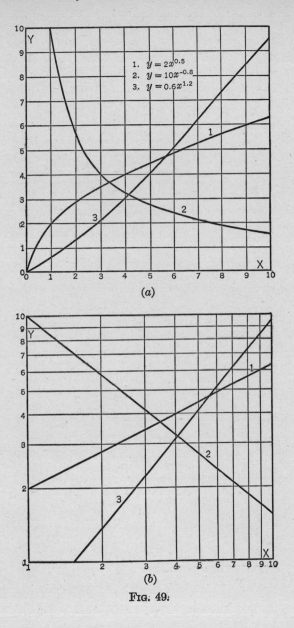

1. $y = 2x^{0.5}$
2. $y = 10x^{-0.8}$
3. $y = 0.6x^{1.2}$

(a)

(b)

FIG. 49.

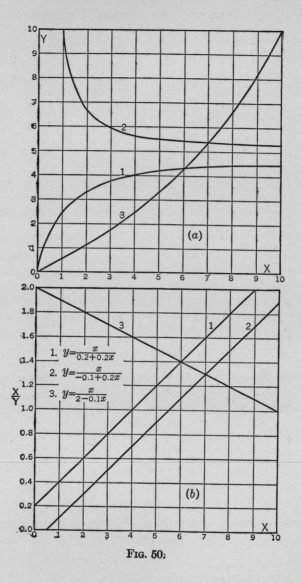

1. $y = \dfrac{x}{0.2 + 0.2x}$

2. $y = \dfrac{x}{-0.1 + 0.2x}$

3. $y = \dfrac{x}{2 - 0.1x}$

Fig. 50.

The horizontal asymptote of the curves of the first two equations is $y = \dfrac{1}{0.2} = 5$; the vertical asymptote of the second equation is $x = \frac{1}{2}$, and $x = 20$ is the vertical asymptote of the third equation.

The equation of the hyperbola may be rewritten in either of the following forms:

$$\frac{x}{y} = a + bx$$

$$\frac{1}{y} = \frac{a}{x} + b$$

These equations show that the curve may be rectified either by plotting $\dfrac{x}{y}$ versus x or $\dfrac{1}{y}$ versus $\dfrac{1}{x}$.   Using the first method, the three curves are replotted in Fig. 50b with $\dfrac{x}{y}$ as ordinate and x as abscissa.   On this new coordinate system each curve becomes a straight line, and the two constants may be determined by finding the equation of this straight line; the slope of the line is $b = \dfrac{\Delta\left(\dfrac{x}{y}\right)}{\Delta x}$, while the intercept on the ordinate axis $(x = 0)$ is the constant a.

(e) *Simple exponential curve*, $y = a(10)^{bx}$.   The equation of the exponential or logarithmic curve may also be written as $y = ae^{2.3026bx}$, where e is the base of Napierian logarithms. When $x = 0$, these exponential curves intersect the Y axis at $y = a$.   If $b = 0$, a straight horizontal line $(y = a)$ results; with positive values of b, the plot of the equation is ascending concave, with negative values of b, the curve is descending concave.

Two exponential curves are plotted in Fig. 51a; the equation of one is $y = 0.2(10)^{0.5x}$, or $y = 0.2(e)^{1.1513x}$, and of the other, $y = 0.9(10)^{-0.8x}$, or $y = 0.9(e)^{-1.8421x}$.

The logarithmic form of the simple exponential equation is

$$\log y = \log a + bx$$

A plot of $\log y$ versus x should be a straight line if an exponential equation fits the data. The intercept of the

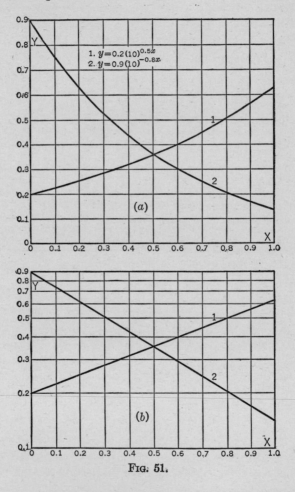

1. $y = 0.2(10)^{0.5x}$
2. $y = 0.9(10)^{-0.8x}$

FIG. 51.

straight line on this coordinate system $(x = 0)$ is $\log y = \log a$, or $y = a$. The slope of the straight line is the constant b, where $b = \dfrac{\Delta(\log y)}{\Delta x}$. The two exponential curves of

Fig 51a are replotted on a semilogarithmic coordinate system[1] (one log scale and one uniform scale) in Fig. 51b.

(f) An illustration of the method of finding the equation of a curve to fit observed data when that equation contains two constants follows. The accompanying table shows the atmospheric pressure observed during the summer at different altitudes, as given in the Smithsonian Tables. An empirical equation is desired that will fit these data over the range of observations.

	Altitude in kilometers, h	Pressure in millimeters of mercury, p	$\log p$	Calculated p	Percentage deviation
	0	760.0	2.8808	760.0	0.00
	1	674.8	2.8292	672.5	−0.34
	2	598.0	2.7767	595.1	−0.48
	3	528.9	2.7234	526.6	−0.43
	4	466.6	2.6689	466.0	−0.13
	5	410.6	2.6134	412.4	+0.44
	6	360.2	2.5565	364.9	+1.30
Σ	21		19.0489		

[1] The following is a partial list of standard arrangements of semilogarithmic cross-section paper (or paper with "ratio" ruling) available in printed form and useful in graphic analysis:

$8\frac{1}{2}$ $in.$ by 11 $in.$ $sheets:$ 1 cycle on 9-in. base by 120 divisions (20 per in.); 2 cycles on $4\frac{1}{2}$-in. base by 120 divisions; 3 cycles on 3-in. base by 120 divisions; 1 cycle on 6-in. base by 180 divisions (20 per in.); 2 cycles on $3\frac{3}{4}$-in. base by 200 divisions (20 per in.).

11 $in.$ by $16\frac{1}{2}$ $in.$ $sheets:$ 1 cycle on 9-in. base by 280 divisions (20 per in.); 2 cycles on $4\frac{1}{2}$-in. base by 280 divisions; 3 cycles on 3-in. base by 280 divisions.

11 $in.$ by 14 $in.$ $sheets:$ 1 cycle on 250-mm. base by 250 divisions (1 mm. apart); 2 cycles on 100-mm. base by 300 divisions (1 mm. apart).

13 $in.$ by $19\frac{1}{2}$ $in.$ $sheets:$ 3 cycles on 90-mm. base by 400 divisions (1 mm. apart).

$19\frac{1}{2}$ $in.$ by $27\frac{1}{2}$ $in.$ $sheets:$ 5 cycles on 90-mm. base by 600 divisions (1 mm. apart).

31 $in.$ by 31 $in.$ $sheets:$ 1.2 cycles (1 to 16) on 500-mm. base by 300 divisions (2 mm. apart); 1.49 cycles (1 to 31) on 400-mm. base by 300 divisions (2 mm. apart); 2 cycles on 300-mm. base by 300 divisions (2 mm. apart).

The data are shown plotted on a coordinate system of uniform scales in Fig. 52a. The curve is descending concave with but a slight curvature; comparing this curve form with the preceding curves shown in this section, the exponential form, $y = a(10)^{bx}$, or $p = a(10)^{bh}$, with a negative value of b is suspected. To verify this, the data are replotted on semi-logarithmic cross-section paper in Fig. 52b; this is equivalent to plotting log p versus h. A straight line is found to fit this

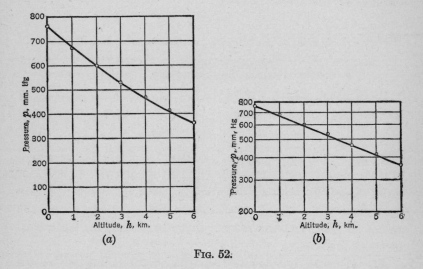

Fig. 52.

plot very well, and the choice of an exponential equation to fit the data is justified.

The value of the constant a is fixed if the equation is to give the standard atmospheric pressure, 760 mm. of mercury, at sea level; in this case, $h = 0$, and $p = a = 760$. With a fixed as 760, the constant b may be found by the method of group averages with residual summation; since there is only one constant to be determined, all the data may be used as one group.

The logarithmic form of the exponential equation is

$$\log p = \log a + bh = 2.8808 + bh$$

The summation of the residuals for the group of seven

observations is zero when

$$\Sigma \log p - 7(2.8808) - b\Sigma h = 0$$

From the table,

$$19.0489 - 20.1656 - 21b = 0$$

$$b = -\frac{1.1167}{21} = -0.0531$$

The empirical equation that fits the above data very closely is

$$p = 760(10)^{-0.0531h}$$

where p = the atmospheric pressure, in millimeters of mercury,

h = the altitude, in kilometers.

With p representing the atmospheric pressure in inches of mercury, and h representing the altitude in thousands of feet,

$$p = 29.92(10)^{-0.0165h}$$

In the table, the values of p calculated from the empirical equation and the percentage deviation of each calculated value from the observed value are shown. The equation summarizes the data with reasonable accuracy over the range of observations given, but should not be extended beyond this range.

52. *Exercises.* Find the empirical equations with two constants that fit the data in the following problems:

(1) The heat content of saturated steam, h, in B.t.u. per pound at different temperatures, t, in degrees Fahrenheit.

t	32	40	50	60	70	80	90	100
h	1073.4	1077.1	1081.7	1086.2	1090.8	1095.3	1099.8	1104.2

t	110	120
h	1108.6	1113.0

Use the method of least squares to obtain the constants.

(2) The heating value of dry Pennsylvania anthracite silt, *HV*, in B.t.u. per pound with different ash contents, *A*, in pounds per pound of dry silt.

HV	12,200	10,750	9400	7600	6700	5950
A	0.175	0.260	0.340	0.445	0.490	0.565

Find the constants by the method of group averages.

(3) The dry-bulb temperature, *t*, in degrees Fahrenheit, and the wet-bulb depression, $t - t'$, in degrees Fahrenheit, for a constant relative humidity of 0.50 at a pressure of 30 in. of mercury, absolute.

t	50	60	70	80	90	100
$t - t'$	7.8	9.5	11.3	13.0	14.7	16.5

(4) The specific volume, *V*, in cubic feet per pound, of saturated steam at different pressures, *p*, in pounds per square inch absolute.

p	30	40	50	60	70	80	90	100	120	140	160	180
V	13.75	10.50	8.51	7.17	6.20	5.47	4.89	4.43	3.73	3.22	2.83	2.53

(5) The friction factor, *f*, for the stream line flow of oil in round pipes at different values of Reynolds' number, *Re*.

Re	300	400	500	600	900	1200
f	0.25	0.18	0.14	0.12	0.08	0.06

(6) The Nusselt number, *Nu*, for heat transfer to air flowing inside pipes at different values of Reynolds' number, *Re*.

Re	3200	4500	6000	12,000	20,000	30,000
Nu	13	17	21	37	52	74

(7) The film coefficient of heat transfer, h, in B.t.u. per hour per square foot per degree Fahrenheit, from a horizontal plate to boiling water at different values of the temperature drop from the plate to the water, Δt, in degrees Fahrenheit.

Δt	11	13.5	16	20	22
h	650	1100	1400	2050	2600

(8) The results of tests on a marine Diesel engine (1250 H.P.), running at the constant speed of 125 r.p.m., giving the brake horsepower, B.H.P., and the mechanical efficiency, e_m.

B.H.P.	200	400	600	800	1000	1200
e_m	0.53	0.64	0.70	0.73	0.76	0.78

(9) A normal induction curve for wrought iron, giving the field intensity, H, in oersteds, and the flux density, B, in gausses.

H	5	10	30	50	70	90
B	11.5	13.0	15.1	16.0	16.2	16.3

(10) The adsorption of SO_2, by silica gel at 32 F.; the per cent by volume of the SO_2 in the entering gas, p; the SO_2 adsorbed by the gel as a percentage of the weight of the gel, S.

p	0	2	4	6	8	10
S	0	8.8	13.7	17.0	18.9	20.4

(11) The pressure of saturated water vapor over ice, p, in inches of mercury, absolute, at the temperature, t, in degrees Fahrenheit.

t	-20	-10	-4	$+5$	$+14$	$+23$
p	0.01264	0.02268	0.03055	0.04886	0.07677	0.11862

(12) The relative humidity, R.H., in per cent, corresponding to the difference between the dry-bulb temperature and the dew point, $t - t_1$, in degrees Fahrenheit.

R.H.	20	30	40	50	60	70	80	90	100
$t - t_1$	46.5	35.0	26.5	20.0	15.0	10.5	6.5	3.0	0

(13) The difference between the temperature of a body cooling in air and the air temperature, θ, in degrees Fahrenheit, at any time, t, in seconds, after the start of cooling.

t	0	10	20	30	40	50	60
θ	130	123	116	109	103	97.5	92

(14) Experiments on drying give the weight of free water, w, as a per cent of the weight of the dry material after the drying time, t, in seconds.

t	0	20	40	60	80	100
w	29.5	18.4	11.9	8.0	5.0	3.3

53. (a) If an equation with two constants that fits the observed data cannot be found, equations containing *three constants* may be necessary, and several of these equations, together with methods of "rectifying" the curves, will be explained.

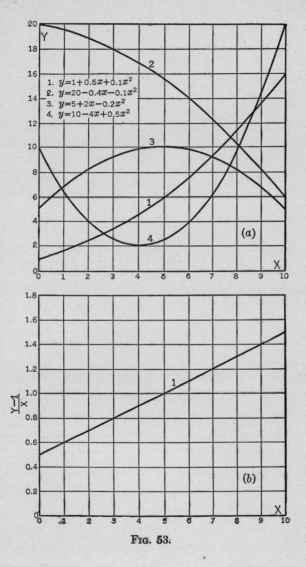

1. $y=1+0.5x+0.1x^2$
2. $y=20-0.4x-0.1x^2$
3. $y=5+2x-0.2x^2$
4. $y=10-4x+0.5x^2$

(a)

(b)

Fig. 53.

(b) The *parabola*, $y = a + bx + cx^2$. This is the equation of the straight line with the added term, cx^2. Four parabolic curves are shown in Fig. 53a. Many experimental results may be fitted by the parabolic equation containing three constants.

There are several methods of "rectifying" these parabolic curves. Let (x_1, y_1) be the coordinates of any point on a smooth curve through the data; then

$$y_1 = a + bx_1 + cx_1^2$$

and
$$y = a + bx + cx^2$$

Subtracting,

$$y - y_1 = bx - bx_1 + cx^2 - cx_1^2$$

Dividing both sides of the equation by $(x - x_1)$

$$\frac{y - y_1}{x - x_1} = b + cx_1 + cx$$

Since $(b + cx_1)$ is a constant, a plot of $\dfrac{y - y_1}{x - x_1}$ versus x will be a straight line, if the data can be fitted by the parabolic equation.

Also, taking the derivative of y in the equation of the parabola gives

$$\frac{dy}{dx} = b + 2cx$$

Therefore, a plot of $\dfrac{\Delta y}{\Delta x}$ versus x, or of Δy versus x, for equidistant values of x, will be a straight line when the parabolic equation fits the data.

In Fig. 53b, curve 1 is replotted by choosing a point on the original curve, $x_1 = 0$ and $y_1 = 1$, and plotting $\dfrac{y - 1}{x}$ versus x. A straight line results, and the student may check this by replotting the other three curves, using any of the above methods to "rectify" them.

(c) *The parabolic or hyperbolic curve, $y = ax^b + c$.* When the data are fitted by a parabola that, unlike those in Fig. 49a, does not pass through the origin, or by a hyperbola that, unlike the one in the same figure, is not asymptotic to the

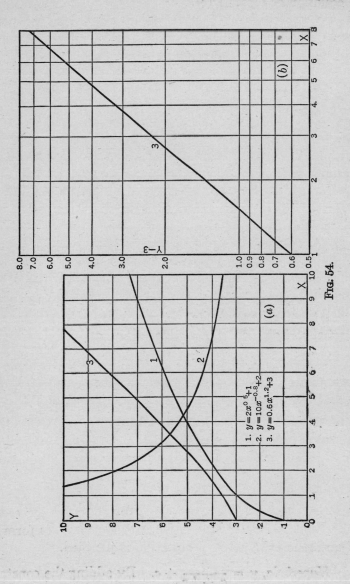

1. $y = 2x^{0.5} + 1$
2. $y = 10x^{-0.8} + 2$
3. $y = 0.6x^{1.2} + 3$

FIG. 54.

coordinate axes, then a constant term, c, may be added to the equation of Sect. 51 (c).

Three curves of this form are shown in Fig 54a; these curves should be compared with those of Fig. 49a. With positive values of b, the constant, c, represents the intercept of the parabola on the Y axis; with negative values of b, $y = c$ is the horizontal asymptote of the hyperbola.

The equation in log form is

$$\log (y - c) = \log a + b \log x$$

A plot of $\log (y - c)$ versus $\log x$ or of $(y - c)$ versus x on logarithmic cross-section paper will be a straight line, if the data can be fitted by the above equation. In Fig. 47b a plot of $(y - 3)$ versus x on log paper shows how curve 3 may be "rectified."

However, the constant c must be determined before the choice of the equation may be verified by this method. If the original equation is parabolic, the intercept of the curve may be found, provided the curve does not have to be extended too far beyond the observations. If the curve is hyperbolic, however, the value of c, or the horizontal asymptote, is very hard to determine. In any case, a general method of finding c is desirable. From a smooth curve drawn through the data, pick *any* two points with coordinates (x_1, y_1) and (x_2, y_2). Find from the curve, the ordinate, y_3, of a point chosen such that $x_3 = \sqrt{x_1 x_2}$. Then, the student may show that

$$c = \frac{y_1 y_2 - y_3^2}{y_1 + y_2 - 2y_3}$$

After c is found, if a plot of $(y - c)$ versus x on log cross-section paper is a straight line, the choice of this form of the parabolic or hyperbolic equation is justified.

(d) *Hyperbola*, $y = \dfrac{x}{a + bx} + c$. By adding the constant c to the equation discussed in Sect. 49 (d), this equation of the hyperbola is obtained. The horizontal asymptote of this hyperbola is $y = \dfrac{1}{b} + c$. The three curves shown in Fig 50a are modified by the algebraic addition of constants and shown in Fig. 55a.

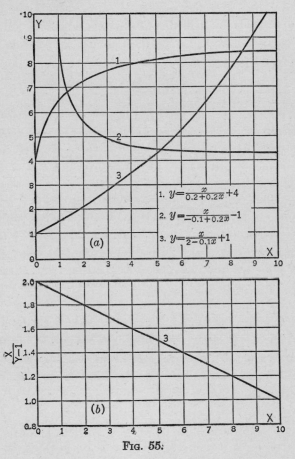

1. $y = \dfrac{x}{0.2 + 0.2x} + 4$

2. $y = \dfrac{x}{0.1 + 0.2x} - 1$

3. $y = \dfrac{x}{2 - 0.1x} + 1$

(a)

(b)

FIG. 55.

To verify whether such a curve will fit the observed data, pick any point (x_1, y_1) on a smooth curve through the data; then

$$y_1 = \frac{x_1}{a + bx_1} + c$$

and

$$y = \frac{x}{a + bx} + c$$

Subtracting $\quad y - y_1 = \dfrac{x}{a + bx} - \dfrac{x_1}{a + bx_1}$

$$= \dfrac{a(x - x_1)}{(a + bx)(a + bx_1)}$$

Then, $\qquad \dfrac{x - x_1}{y - y_1} = (a + bx_1) + x\left(b + \dfrac{b^2 x_1}{a}\right)$

Since $(a + bx_1)$ and $\left(b + \dfrac{b^2 x_1}{a}\right)$ are constants, a plot of

$\dfrac{x - x_1}{y - y_1}$ versus x will be a straight line. This is shown in

Fig. 55b for curve 3, only; in this case the intercept is the

chosen point, or $x_1 = 0$ and $y_1 = 1$. A plot of $\dfrac{x}{y - 1}$ versus

x is then shown to be a straight line.

(e) *Exponential curve*, $y = a(10)^{bx} + c$. This equation is
obtained by adding the constant c to the simple exponential
equation given in Sect. 51 (e). In this case, the shapes of the
curves are similar to those shown in Fig. 51a, and the
student may readily visualize the effect of the algebraic
addition of a constant to each value of y for a given value
of x.

The logarithmic form of this exponential equation is

$$\log (y - c) = \log a + bx$$

A plot of $\log (y - c)$ versus x or a plot of $(y - c)$ versus x
on semilog cross-section paper should be a straight line when
the data are fitted by the above equation. To determine
the constant c, take any two points on a smooth curve
through the data with coordinates (x_1, y_1) and (x_2, y_2); from
this curve, find the value of the ordinate, y_3, at a point where
$x_3 = \dfrac{x_1 + x_2}{2}$. Then the student may show that

$$c = \dfrac{y_1 y_2 - y_3{}^2}{y_1 + y_2 - 2y_3}$$

(f) *The exponential curve*, $y = a(10)^{bx + cx^2}$. This equation,
like the parabolic, $y = a + bx + cx^2$, may be made to fit a

large variety of curve shapes by proper choice of the three constants. All the preceding exponential curves have been either ascending concave or descending concave; this equation will fit ascending convex or concave, descending convex

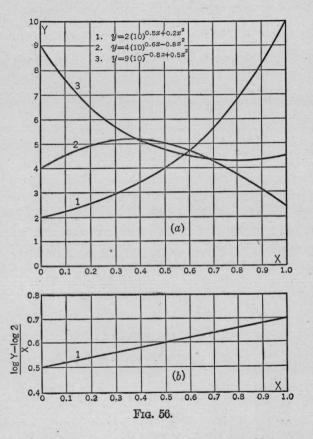

1. $y = 2(10)^{0.5x + 0.2x^2}$
2. $y = 4(10)^{0.6x - 0.8x^2}$
3. $y = 9(10)^{-0.8x + 0.5x^2}$

(a)

(b)

FIG. 56.

or concave, ascending-descending, or descending-ascending curves. The curves for three equations are shown in Fig. 56a.

The logarithmic form of this equation is

$$\log y = \log a + bx + cx^2$$

Hence,

$$\frac{d(\log y)}{dx} = b + 2cx$$

The student may readily show that a plot of $\dfrac{\log y - \log y_1}{x - x_1}$ versus x, where (x_1, y_1) are the coordinates of any point on a smooth curve through the data, will approximate a straight line when the data are fitted by a curve of this form. Also, a plot of $\dfrac{\Delta(\log y)}{\Delta x}$ versus x, or of $\Delta(\log y)$, for equidistant values of x, versus x will be a straight line. In Fig. 56b, curve 1 is rectified by choosing the point, $x_1 = 0$ and $y_1 = 2$, and plotting $\dfrac{\log y - \log 2}{x}$ versus x; this is equivalent to plotting $(0.5 + 0.2x)$ versus x, in this case.

(g) As an illustration of the method of obtaining the constants in an equation containing three constants, an empirical equation will next be fitted to the experimental results given in the table relating the total head, H, in feet, imparted to water by a centrifugal pump, and the capacity, Q, in gallons per minute, all for the constant speed of 1100 r.p.m.

	Capacity, Q	Q^2	Total head, H	$H - 98$	$\dfrac{H - 98}{Q}$	Calculated H
	0	0	98	0		98.3
	20	400	106	8	0.400	106.4
	40	1,600	112	14	0.350	111.6
	60	3,600	114	16	0.267	113.8
Σ	120	5,600	430			
	80	6,400	113	15	0.188	113.0
	100	10,000	110	12	0.120	109.0
	120	14,400	102	4	0.033	102.6
	140	19,600	92	−6	−0.043	92.9
Σ	440	50,400	417			
	160	25,600	79	−19	−0.119	80.4
	180	32,400	64	−34	−0.189	64.7
	200	40,000	47	−51	−0.255	46.3
Σ	540	98,000	190			

In Fig. 57a, the total head, H, is plotted against the capacity, Q. Comparing this curve with the others shown in this section, it appears as if a parabolic curve of the form, $H = a + bQ + cQ^2$, might fit this ascending-descending con-

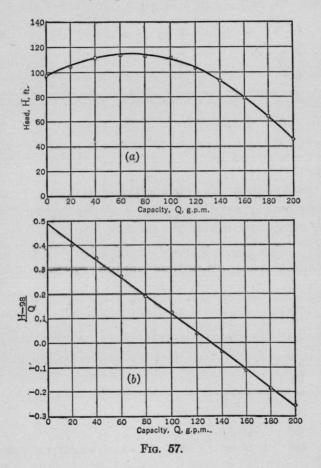

FIG. 57.

vex curve. To verify this, choose the point, $Q = 0$ and $H = 98$, and plot $\dfrac{H - 98}{Q}$ against Q as in Fig. 57b. A straight line fits the data on this coordinate system, verifying the original choice of an equation of the parabolic form.

To determine the constants, a, b, and c, by the use of the method of group averages, break up the data into three groups as in the table. Then, for each group, set the summation of the residuals equal to zero, or

$$\Sigma H - \Sigma(a + bQ + cQ^2) = 0$$

For the first group, $430 - 4a - 120b - 5600c = 0$
for the second group, $417 - 4a - 440b - 50,400c = 0$
and for the third group, $\underline{190 - 3a - 540b - 98,000c = 0}$

From a simultaneous solution of these three equations,

$$a = 98.3, \ b = 0.48, \quad \text{and} \quad c = -0.0037$$

The empirical equation is $H = 98.3 + 0.48Q - 0.0037Q^2$, and the values calculated from this equation shown in the table may be compared with the observed values of head.

54. As a short summary of the work in the preceding sections on empirical equations, the accompanying table gives in the second column the form of the equation fitting the data when they plot as a straight line with the method of plotting given in the first column. In this table, the subscripts 1 and 2 refer to *any* points on the experimental curve, and the subscript 3 to a point on this curve *chosen* as indicated.

If the data plot as a straight line on a coordinate system of	the form of the equation fitting the data is
y versus x	$y = a + bx$
$\log y$ versus $\log x$	$y = ax^b$
$\log y$ versus x	$y = a(10)^{bx}$
$\dfrac{x}{y}$ versus x	$y = \dfrac{x}{a + bx}$
$\dfrac{y - y_1}{x - x_1}$ versus x	$y = a + bx + cx^2$
$\dfrac{x - x_1}{y - y_1}$ versus x	$y = \dfrac{x}{a + bx} + c$
$\dfrac{\log y - \log y_1}{x - x_1}$ versus x	$y = a(10)^{bx+cx^2}$
$\log (y - c)$ versus $\log x$, where $c = \dfrac{y_1 y_2 - y_3^2}{y_1 + y_2 - 2y_3}$, when $x_3 = \sqrt{x_1 x_2}$	$y = ax^b + c$
$\log (y - c)$ versus x, where $c = \dfrac{y_1 y_2 - y_3^2}{y_1 + y_2 - 2y_3}$, when $x_3 = \dfrac{x_1 + x_2}{2}$	$y = a(10)^{bx} + c$

55. *Exercises.* Find the empirical equations that fit the data in the following problems:

(1) Experimental values of the mean specific heat per mol at constant pressure for CO_2, C_p, for the range from 0 to t degrees Centigrade.

t	0	400	800	1200	1600	2000
C_p	8.9	10.0	10.9	11.6	12.1	12.3

(2) The mean coefficient of thermal expansion of mercury, A, between 0 and t degrees Centigrade.

t	100	150	200	250	300
A	0.00018216	0.00018261	0.00018323	0.00018403	0.00018500

(3) The observed maximum load per unit area, $\dfrac{P}{A}$, in pounds per square inch, carried by short columns of cold-rolled steel with various slenderness ratios, $\dfrac{L}{K}$, inches per inch.

$\dfrac{L}{K}$	20	30	40	50	60	70
$\dfrac{P}{A}$	90,000	86,500	84,000	79,500	70,000	58,000

(4) The observed moisture in wet steam, m, per cent by weight, at different rates of steam generation, R, in pounds per hour per cubic foot of steam space.

R	250	500	900	1200	1600	2000
m	0.10	0.28	0.80	1.38	2.56	4.10

(5) Tests on the friction between a straw-fiber driver and an iron driven wheel under a load of 400 lb. giving slip, s, in percentage, and coefficient of friction, f.

s	0.65	0.93	1.16	1.80	2.12	3.00
f	0.129	0.275	0.318	0.400	0.410	0.435

(6) The percentage by volume of CO_2 in the dry products of combustion, p, in burning fuel oil with different amounts of excess air, x, in percentage.

x	0	20	40	60	80	100
p	16.0	13.2	11.2	9.8	8.7	7.8

(7) An experiment on the cooling of water in air giving the temperature of the water, θ, in degrees Fahrenheit, and the time after the beginning of the observations, t, in minutes.

t	0	1	2	3	4	5	10
θ	190	177	165	155	147	140	118

(8) The comparative efficiency of Florida fuller's earth in decolorizing Pennsylvania steam-refined stock, e, in percentage, after being reburned or revivified n times in a rotary kiln.

n	1	2	3	4	5	6	7	8
e	100	87	77	68	62	57	53	50

(9) The saturation pressure, p, in pounds per square inch absolute, for carbon dioxide at the absolute temperature, T, degrees Fahrenheit.

T	440	460	480	500	520	540	548.4
p	221	308	422	565	744	965	1070

(10) The volume of air (measured at 0 C. and 760 mm. of mercury, absolute), V, in cubic centimeters in a saturated solution of 1000 cc. of water at normal barometric pressure corresponding to the temperature, t, in degrees Centigrade.

t	0	5	10	15	20	25
V	29.18	25.68	22.84	20.55	18.68	17.08

56. When none of the preceding equations will fit all the experimental data, the data may either be broken up into two or more groups and an equation fitted to each group, or a polynomial equation of the form, $y = a + bx + cx^2 + dx^3 + \ldots + kx^n$, may be forced to fit the data. If the data are broken up into several groups and an equation derived for each group, the limits over which each equation applies must be clearly specified.

To fit a polynomial equation to the data, select $n + 1$ points on the experimental curve and substitute the $n + 1$ simultaneous values of x and y in the polynomial equation. Solve these equations to find the values of the $n + 1$ constants, i.e., a, b, c, d, etc.

By taking enough terms in the polynomial, this equation may be forced to fit many experimental results, but it is always easier and often just as accurate to use the equations explained in preceding sections.

57. *Exercises.* Find the constants in polynomial equations that fit the following data:

(1) The ultimate strength, P, in pounds, of ropes with diameter, d, in inches, made from Manila hemp.

d	$\frac{1}{2}$	$\frac{3}{4}$	1	$1\frac{1}{4}$	$1\frac{1}{2}$	$1\frac{3}{4}$	2
P	1900	4100	7100	10,900	15,000	19,800	25,100

(2) The indicated horsepower of the engines, P, and the speed, v, in knots, of a battleship.

v	8	10	12	14	16	18
P	1150	1850	3200	5450	8950	14,200

58. (a) When more than two variables are involved in the results of an experiment, an empirical relation connecting the several variables may often be found. If three variables are involved, one variable may be plotted against the second, and lines representing different constant values of the third variable may be drawn on this coordinate system. By using methods described in the preceding section, the constants in the empirical two-variable equations of these lines may be found; these constants may then be plotted against the third variable, and the empirical equations giving the relation between these constants and the third variable determined.

(b) As an illustration of the method, an empirical equation will be fitted to the data given in the accompanying table, which shows the capacity of steam traps. Three variables are involved, viz., the diameter of the valve orifice, d; the steam pressure, p; and the weight of water discharged per hour, w. First, d may be plotted against w for each constant value of p. When this plot is made on cross-section paper with uniform scales, the curves are parabolic in form (note that, for all pressures, w will be zero when d is zero). By plotting d against w on logarithmic cross-section paper, each curve for a constant pressure becomes a straight line, as shown in Fig. 58a. The general form of the relation be-

Diameter of valve orifice, inches d	Steam pressure, pounds per square inch gage p	Weight of water discharged per hour, pounds w
$\frac{1}{4}$	50	3,114
	75	3,811
	100	4,402
	125	4,976
$\frac{5}{16}$	50	4,847
	75	5,936
	100	6,853
	125	7,662
$\frac{11}{32}$	50	5,883
	75	7,205
	100	8,320
	125	9,302
$\frac{3}{8}$	50	6,998
	75	8,579
	100	9,986
	125	11,075
$\frac{7}{16}$	50	9,535
	75	11,680
	100	13,486
	125	15,073
$\frac{1}{2}$	50	12,537
	75	15,252
	100	17,616
	125	19,694

tween d and w for constant p is, then, $d = aw^b$. Further-
more, the lines in Fig. 58a are apparently parallel, which
means that the value of b is substantially the same for all
pressures. By breaking the data up into two groups, each
group containing three diameters of the valve orifice, the
constants a and b may be obtained for each of the four
pressures by the method of group averages with residual

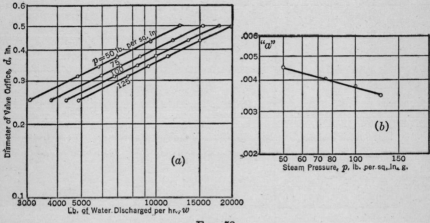

FIG. 58.

summation. The results of these calculations are shown in
the following short table:

p	a	b
50	0.00449	0.498
75	0.00405	0.499
100	0.00378	0.498
125	0.00356	0.501

For all pressures, the exponent b may be taken as 0.5
without appreciable error; then $d = aw^{0.5}$, where a is a
function of the pressure. When a is plotted against p on
cross-section paper with uniform scales, the curve is apparently hyperbolic. This curve can be straightened out by

plotting a against p on logarithmic cross-section paper, as shown in Fig. 58b. The equation relating a and p is of the form $a = mp^n$, where n is negative. By breaking up the data given in the above table into two groups with two pressures in each group, the constants m and n are found by the method of group averages to be 0.0119 and -0.25, respectively. Hence, $a = 0.0119p^{-0.25}$. Substituting this value of a in the original equation, we find that $d = 0.0119p^{-0.25}w^{0.5}$, or $w = 7056p^{0.5}d^2$. This empirical equation summarizes the data given in the original table with fair accuracy.

If the value of the exponent b had not been the same for all pressures, the empirical relation connecting b with pressure could have been found in the same manner as the equation for a.

59. *Exercises.* Find empirical formulas to fit the following data involving three variables:

(1)

Dry-bulb temperature, degrees Fahrenheit	Wet-bulb depression, degrees Fahrenheit	Relative humidity, per cent
40	2	83
	4	68
	6	52
	8	37
50	2	87
	4	74
	6	61
	8	49
	10	38
60	2	89
	4	78
	6	68
	8	58
	10	48
70	3	86
	6	72
	9	59
	12	48
	15	36
80	3	87
	6	75
	9	64
	12	54
	15	44
90	4	85
	8	71
	12	58
	16	47
	20	36
100	4	86
	8	73
	12	62
	16	51
	20	41

(2)

Effective temperature	Dry-bulb temperature, degrees Fahrenheit	Wet-bulb temperature, degrees Fahrenheit
60	60	60
	62	54
	64	47
	66	41
65	65	65
	66	63
	68	59
	70	54
	72	49
70	70	70
	72	67
	74	64
	76	61
	78	57
75	75	75
	78	72
	80	70
	82	67
	84	64
	86	62
	88	59
80	80	80
	84	77
	88	73
	92	70
	96	66

(3)

Depth of heater, in rows of tubing	Velocity of air through net face area, in feet per second	Friction drop in pressure of air flowing through extended surface heater, inches of water
1	5.00	0.030
	6.67	0.050
	8.33	0.074
	10.00	0.103
	11.67	0.136
	13.33	0.174
2	5.00	0.044
	6.67	0.076
	8.33	0.116
	10.00	0.164
	11.67	0.221
	13.33	0.285
3	5.00	0.058
	6.67	0.101
	8.33	0.158
	10.00	0.225
	11.07	0.306
	13.33	0.396
4	5.00	0.072
	6.67	0.127
	8.33	0.200
	10.00	0.286
	11.67	0.391
	13.33	0.507
5	5.00	0.087
	6.67	0.153
	8.33	0.241
	10.00	0.347
	11.67	0.476
	13.33	0.618
6	5.00	0.101
	6.67	0.178
	8.33	0.283
	10.00	0.408
	11.67	0.561
	13.33	0.729

CHAPTER VI

EMPIRICAL EQUATIONS — PERIODIC CURVES

60. (*a*) Curves which are composed of the repetition of values of one of the variables at regular, repeated intervals of a second variable are described as periodic. Examples of periodic curves are the plots of alternating current and voltage versus time and the space-time, velocity-time, and acceleration-time curves of simple harmonic motion. Periodic curves may be represented by periodic functions of one of the variables. If the range of the variable, x, in which one complete cycle of the second variable, y, occurs be called the *period* and given the symbol Δx_p, a periodic function is one such that

$$y = f(x + \Delta x_p) = f(x)$$

For example, if x represents an angle in radians, $\sin x$ and $\cos x$ have a period of $\Delta x_p = 2\pi$, since $\sin (x + 2\pi) = \sin x$ and $\cos (x + 2\pi) = \cos x$. Note, however, if x represents the angle in degrees, $\sin x$ and $\cos x$ have a period of $\Delta x_p = 360$. As another illustration, assume a varying temperature, y, repeats itself every 24 hours; then if x represents time in hours, this periodic function has a period of Δx_p 24.

(*b*) If θ represents an angle in radians, any single-valued periodic function of θ which is finite in the period, $\Delta\theta_p = 2\pi$, except for a finite number of discontinuities, may be represented by an infinite trigonometric series (or Fourier series) of the general form

$$
\begin{aligned}
y = f(\theta) = y_m &+ a_1 \cos \theta + a_2 \cos 2\theta + \cdots \\
&+ a_n \cos n\theta + \cdots \\
&+ b_1 \sin \theta + b_2 \sin 2\theta + \cdots \\
&+ b_n \sin n\theta + \cdots \qquad (70)
\end{aligned}
$$

The empirical equation then contains a finite number of terms, as many terms of the infinite series as are necessary to give the desired accuracy in the representation of the function.

When the function $y = f(\theta)$ is known, the various constants in the series may be found as follows

$$y_m = \frac{\int_0^{2\pi} y \, d\theta}{2\pi} \quad ; \quad \cdots \cdots \cdots \cdots \cdots \quad (71)$$

$$a_k = \frac{\int_0^{2\pi} y \cos k\theta \, d\theta}{\pi} \quad ; \quad \cdots \cdots \cdots \cdots \cdots \quad (72)$$

$$b_k = \frac{\int_0^{2\pi} y \sin k\theta \, d\theta}{\pi} \quad ; \quad \cdots \cdots \cdots \cdots \cdots \quad (73)$$

The trigonometric series may be written entirely in terms of cosines or sines of the angle x expressed in radians. To demonstrate this fact for cosine terms, note that

$$y = a_k \cos k\theta + b_k \sin k\theta$$

$$= \sqrt{a_k{}^2 + b_k{}^2} \left(\frac{a_k}{\sqrt{a_k{}^2 + b_k{}^2}} \cos k\theta + \frac{b_k}{\sqrt{a_k{}^2 + b_k{}^2}} \sin k\theta \right)$$

Let $\quad \sqrt{a_k{}^2 + b_k{}^2} = c_k \quad \cdots \cdots \cdots \cdots \cdots \quad (74)$

and $\qquad\qquad \phi_k = \tan^{-1} \dfrac{b_k}{a_k} \quad \cdots \cdots \cdots \cdots \quad (75)$

Then, $\qquad y = c_k (\cos \phi_k \cos k\theta + \sin \phi_k \sin k\theta)$

or $\qquad\qquad y = c_k \cos (k\theta - \phi_k)$

This wave is called the kth harmonic with amplitude c_k and phase ϕ_k; the period of this wave is $\dfrac{2\pi}{k}$ for

$$\cos \left[k \left(\theta + \frac{2\pi}{k} \right) - \phi_k \right] = \cos (k\theta + 2\pi - \phi_k) = \cos (k\theta - \phi_k)$$

When $k = 1$, the wave that results is called the *fundamental* wave; when $k = 2$, the wave is the second harmonic; when $k = 3$, the wave is the third harmonic, etc.

The infinite trigonometric series may also be written, then, as

$$y = y_m + c_1 \cos (\theta - \phi_1) + c_2 \cos (2\theta - \phi_2)$$
$$+ c_3 \cos (3\theta - \phi_3) + \cdots$$
$$+ c_n \cos (n\theta - \phi_n) + \cdots \quad . \quad . \quad (76)$$

This is the form that will be used in the discussion that follows.

61. (a) When the values y are known for a periodic function, $f(x)$, for different values of x, an empirical equation fitting the results may be found by evaluating the mean term, y_m, and the amplitudes and phases of the fundamental and later harmonics, c_1, ϕ_1, c_2, ϕ_2, in Eq. (76). Determine the period of the function, or the range in the value of x, Δx_p, in which one complete cycle of y occurs. The variable x need not be an angle; frequently this variable in a periodic function will be time, but, in general, may be any quantity. To define an angle in terms of the variable, x, determine the period of the function, Δx_p, or the range of x in which one complete cycle occurs.

Then
$$\theta = mx; \quad \ldots \ldots \ldots \quad (77)$$

for θ in degrees,
$$m = \frac{360}{\Delta x_p} \quad \ldots \ldots \ldots \quad (78a)$$

for θ in radians,
$$m = \frac{2\pi}{\Delta x_p} \quad \ldots \ldots \ldots \quad (78b)$$

Divide x into n equal intervals over the period and read the n ordinates of the curve, as y_0 at x_0, y_1 at x_1, etc. Then y_m is the average value of the n ordinates, and a_k or b_k is twice the average value of the products formed by multiplying each ordinate by the *cosine* or *sine* of k times the corresponding value of θ, or

$$y_m = \frac{1}{n} \Sigma y = \frac{1}{n} (y_0 + y_1 + \cdots + y_{n-1}) \quad \ldots \ldots \quad (79)$$

$$a_k = \frac{2}{n} \Sigma (y \cos k\theta) = \frac{2}{n} (y_0 \cos k\theta_0 + y_1 \cos k\theta_1 + \cdots$$
$$+ y_{n-1} \cos k\theta_{n-1}) \quad . \quad . \quad (80)$$

$$b_k = \frac{2}{n} \Sigma(y \sin k\theta) = \frac{2}{n} (y_0 \sin k\theta_0 + y_1 \sin k\theta_1 + \cdots$$
$$+ y_{n-1} \sin k\theta_{n-1}) \quad . \quad . \quad (81)$$

$$c_k = \sqrt{a_k{}^2 + b_k{}^2} \quad . \ . \ . \ . \ . \ . \ . \ . \ . \ . \ . \ . \ . \ . \ (82)$$

$$\phi_k = \tan^{-1}\frac{b_k}{a_k} \quad . \ . \ . \ . \ . \ . \ . \ . \ . \ . \ . \ . \ . \ . \ (83)$$

where $\sin \phi_k$ has the sign of b_k and $\cos \phi_k$ has the sign of a_k.

(b) As an illustration of the method of determining the constants in an empirical periodic equation, assume that the temperature of the outdoor air has a 24-hour period with values y at the different times, measured in hours after noon, of x given in the table on p. 146 and in Fig. 59. Since Δx_p is 24 hours, if θ is expressed in degrees, from Eq. (78a)

$$m = \frac{360}{24} = 15$$

Then, from Eq. (77)

$$\theta = 15x$$

The time, after noon, has been divided into $n = 24$ equal intervals, and from Eq. (79)

$$y_m = \frac{1}{24}(y_0 + y_1 + \cdots + y_{23})$$

From Eq. (80)

$$a_1 = \frac{1}{12} (y_0 \cos 15x_0 + y_1 \cos 15x_1 + \cdots + y_{23} \cos 15x_{23}),$$

and

$$a_2 = \frac{1}{12} (y_0 \cos 30x_0 + y_1 \cos 30x_1 + \cdots + y_{23} \cos 30x_{23}).$$

From Eq. (81)

$$b_1 = \frac{1}{12} (y_0 \sin 15x_0 + y_1 \sin 15x_1 + \cdots + y_{23} \sin 15x_{23}),$$

and

$$b_2 = \frac{1}{12} (y_0 \sin 30x_0 + y_1 \sin 30x_1 + \cdots + y_{23} \sin 30x_{23}).$$

CALCULATING TABLE (HARMONIC ANALYSIS)

Hours after noon x	Temp. of outdoor air, deg. F. y	cos 15x	y(cos 15x)	sin 15x	y(sin 15x)	cos 30x	y(cos 30x)	sin 30x	y(sin 30x)	Temp. calculated from empirical equation
0	93.7	1.0000	93.70	0.0000	0	1.0000	93.70	0.0000	0	93.7
1	95.2	0.9659	91.95	0.2588	24.64	0.8660	82.44	0.5000	47.60	95.2
2	95.5	0.8660	82.70	0.5000	47.75	0.5000	47.75	0.8660	82.70	95.5
3	94.5	0.7071	66.82	0.7071	66.82	0.0000	0	1.0000	94.50	94.5
4	92.5	0.5000	46.25	0.8660	80.11	-0.5000	-46.25	0.8660	80.11	92.6
5	90.0	0.2588	23.29	0.9659	86.93	-0.8660	-77.94	0.5000	45.00	90.1
6	87.2	0.0000	0	1.0000	87.20	-1.0000	-87.20	0.0000	0	87.2
7	84.2	-0.2588	-21.79	0.9659	81.33	-0.8660	-72.92	-0.5000	-42.10	84.2
8	81.0	-0.5000	-40.50	0.8660	70.15	-0.5000	-40.50	-0.8660	-70.15	81.1
9	78.1	-0.7071	-55.22	0.7071	55.22	0.0000	0	-1.0000	-78.10	78.1
10	75.2	-0.8660	-65.12	0.5000	37.60	0.5000	37.60	-0.8660	-65.12	75.3
11	72.5	-0.9659	-70.03	0.2588	18.76	0.8660	62.79	-0.5000	-36.25	72.5
12	69.9	-1.0000	-69.90	0.0000	0	1.0000	69.90	0.0000	0	69.9
13	67.7	-0.9659	-65.39	-0.2588	-17.52	0.8660	58.63	0.5000	33.85	67.6
14	66.0	-0.8660	-57.16	-0.5000	-33.00	0.5000	33.00	0.8660	57.16	65.9
15	65.0	-0.7071	-45.96	-0.7071	-45.96	0.0000	0	1.0000	65.00	65.0
16	65.2	-0.5000	-32.60	-0.8660	-56.46	-0.5000	-32.60	0.8660	56.46	65.2
17	66.7	-0.2588	-17.26	-0.9659	-64.43	-0.8660	-57.76	0.5000	33.35	66.6
18	69.2	0.0000	0	-1.0000	-69.20	-1.0000	-69.20	0.0000	0	69.2
19	73.0	0.2588	18.89	-0.9659	-70.51	-0.8660	-63.22	-0.5000	-36.50	73.0
20	77.5	0.5000	38.75	-0.8660	-67.12	-0.5000	-38.75	-0.8660	-67.12	77.5
21	82.2	0.7071	58.12	-0.7071	-58.12	0.0000	0	-1.0000	-82.20	82.3
22	86.9	0.8660	75.26	-0.5000	-43.45	0.5000	43.45	-0.8660	-75.26	86.9
23	90.8	0.9659	87.70	-0.2588	-23.50	0.8660	78.63	-0.5000	-45.40	90.8
Σ	1919.7		142.50		107.24		21.55		-2.47	

A tabular form of calculation is shown which is convenient in obtaining the various products and their sums. From the sums obtained in the table,

$$y_m = \frac{1919.7}{24} = 80.0$$

$$a_1 = \frac{142.50}{12} = 11.88$$

$$b_1 = \frac{107.24}{12} = 8.94$$

From Eq. (82)

$$c_1 = \sqrt{(11.88)^2 + (8.94)^2} = 14.9$$

From Eq. (83)

$$\phi_1 = \tan^{-1}\frac{8.94}{11.88} = 37°$$

$$a_2 = \frac{21.55}{12} = 1.80$$

$$b_2 = \frac{-2.47}{12} = -0.21$$

$$c_2 = \sqrt{(1.80)^2 + (-0.21)^2} = 1.8$$

$$\phi_2 = \tan^{-1}\frac{-0.21}{1.80} = 353°$$

(Since the sine is negative and the cosine is positive, ϕ_2 is in the fourth quadrant.)

From Eq. (76), the empirical periodic equation that fits these data is

$$y = 80.0 + 14.9 \cos (15x - 37) + 1.8 \cos (30x - 353)$$

Values of y calculated from this equation at each hour after noon are shown in the table for comparison with the original data; the difference at any hour is never greater than 0.1° F.

In this case, a satisfactory fit has been obtained without going to any harmonics after the second. In many instances, however, it may be found necessary to use more harmonics.

In Fig. 59, the equation is shown plotted with temperature as ordinate and time as abscissa. At any abscissa the
ordinate of the periodic function is the sum of three ordinates: (1) the mean ordinate, $y_m = 80.0$ (in this case);
(2) the fundamental or first harmonic ordinate; (3) the
second harmonic ordinate. Note that the period of the
fundamental wave is the same as that of the original function (24 hours in this case), while the period of the second
harmonic wave is one-half as great (12 hours in this case).

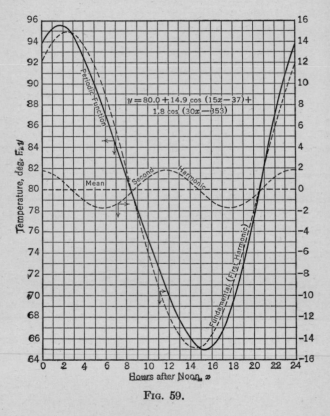

$$y = 80.0 + 14.9 \cos(15x - 37) + 1.8 \cos(30x - 353)$$

Fig. 59.

62. Exercises. Find the empirical equations that fit the
data in the following problems:

(1) The intensity of solar radiation on surfaces in each of the
following positions at 40° North latitude on August 1, I, in

B.t.u. per square foot per hour at different sun times, t, in hours after noon (the period is 24 hours).

t	I			
	East	South	West	Horizontal
16	0	0	0	0
17	6	2	2	5
18	56	4	4	20
19	162	11	11	85
20	211	29	17	160
21	195	74	21	212
22	152	103	24	244
23	94	124	26	281
0	26	128	26	290
1	26	124	94	281
2	24	103	152	244
3	21	74	195	212
4	17	29	211	160
5	11	11	162	85
6	4	4	56	20
7	2	2	6	5
8–16	0	0	0	0

(2) The e.m.f., e, in volts, of an alternating current with a frequency of 60 cycles per second at the time, t, in seconds (the period is 1/60 sec.).

t	0	$\frac{1}{720}$	$\frac{2}{720}$	$\frac{3}{720}$	$\frac{4}{720}$	$\frac{5}{720}$	$\frac{6}{720}$	$\frac{7}{720}$	$\frac{8}{720}$	$\frac{9}{720}$	$\frac{10}{720}$	$\frac{11}{720}$
e	0	21	27	33	38	30	0	−21	−27	−33	−38	−30

(3) The alternating current, i, in amperes, and the angular displacement of the revolving vector, θ, in degrees (the period is 360 degrees).

θ	0	30	60	90	120	150	180	210	240	270	300	330
i	10	15	17	23	37	31	15	4	−8	−13	−14	−6

(4) The rate of solar heat gain, q, in B.t.u. per square foot per hour through glass blocks facing west at north latitude of 40 de-

grees at different sun times, t, in hours after noon. (The period is 24 hours.)

t	18	20	22	0	2	4	6	8–18
q	0	0	6	10	24	65	24	0

(5) The rate of heat transfer, q, in B.t.u. per square foot per hour, of an 8-in. brick wall facing south at different sun times, t, in hours after noon (the period is 24 hours).

t	0	2	4	6	8	10	12	14	16	18	20	22
q	−0.3	2.9	7.0	8.4	7.2	3.8	2.1	1.0	0.7	−0.2	−0.6	−0.9

(6) The equivalent temperature of the outdoor air, t, in degrees Fahrenheit, for a sunlit wall facing east at different sun times, θ, in hours after noon.

θ	0	2	4	6	8	10	12	14	16	18	20	22
t	96	97	96	90	85	82	80	78	76	86	118	114

(7) The approximate difference between the temperature of the air and the temperature of the earth at a depth of 4 feet, Δt, in degrees Fahrenheit during different months of the year, m, with January 1 taken as 0 (the period is 12 months).

m	0	1	2	3	4	5	6	7	8	9	10	11
t	−14	−11	−7	−2	3	7	7	3	−1	−6	−12	−15

INDEX

152   INDEX

I

Index line, 50
Intersection charts, 35

L

Least squares, evaluation of constants
by the method of, 106, 108
Line coordinate charts, 55
Logarithmic scales, 1, 4

M

Modulus, scale, 1

N

Network chart, with five variables, 46
with four variables, 39, 43
with logarithmic scales, 48
with three variables, 35

P

Paper, cross-section with ratio ruling,
115
logarithmic cross-section, 38
Parabola, 109, 121, 122
Periodic function, 142
Polynomial equation, 134
Psychrometric chart, 96, 102
Pump, evaluation of constants in an
empirical equation for imparted
head, 128

R

" Rectification " of curves, 105, 130,
131

S

Scale, equation of, 2
graphical, 1
Scales, sliding, 8
stationary adjacent, 2

Selected points, evaluation of constants by the method of, 106
Semi-logarithmic cross-section paper,
115
Slide rule, for five variables, 25
for four variables, 20
for more than six variables, 28
for six variables, 27
for three variables, 13
special purpose, 12
with groove scale, 31
with stationary log log and sliding
log scale, 11
with two logarithmic scales, 11
with two reciprocal scales, 11
with two squared scales, 10
with two uniform scales, 9
Steam traps, evaluation of constants
in empirical equation for capacity of, 136
Straight line, equation of, 109

T

Temperature difference, alignment
chart for logarithmic mean, 88
Thermometers, Z chart for emergent
stem correction of, 67

V

Velocity, adjacent scales for conversion into velocity head of, 3
Viscosity of gases, line coordinate
chart for, 57

W

Weir, alignment chart for rate of discharge over contracted, 79
alignment chart for rate of discharge over suppressed, 53